CRITICAL PATH ANALYSIS

Over the past years there has been a growing need for more effective planning and control of projects within the private and public sectors. Critical Path Analysis is the organized application of system reasoning for planning, scheduling, and controlling practical situations where many separate jobs, which make up the whole task, can happen simultaneously, almost simultaneously or in sequence such that it is difficult intuitively to establish the relationship between the separate jobs.

The object of this book is to give the reader a practical appreciation of CPA. After finishing the book the reader should also be able to apply the technique successfully. The text is aimed at a basic level, and throughout the text the points made are illustrated, where applicable, to the 'Marketing a New Product' exercise. Graded exercises are also included to ensure that the reader has grasped the pertinent points.

Some other Teach Yourself Books

TEACH YOURSELF BOOKS

CRITICAL PATH ANALYSIS

Techniques, Exercises, and Problems

Douglas W. Lang,

B.Sc., A.M.B.I.M.

*Senior Lecturer, Polytechnic School of Management Studies.
Consultant with Lockyer & Partners Ltd. in association with
Harold Whitehead & Partners Ltd, London W.1.*

TEACH YOURSELF BOOKS

ST PAUL'S HOUSE WARWICK LANE LONDON EC4

First Printed 1970

ISBN 0 340 11450 9

Printed and bound in Great Britain for The English
Universities Press Ltd at The Pitman Press, Bath

TO LORNA

ACKNOWLEDGEMENTS

I am indebted to my colleagues:

Ronald Edgerton	Polytechnic School of Management Studies, London W.1.
Bill Gage	Polytechnic School of Management Studies, London W.1.
Keith Lockyer	Loughborough University, Leicestershire.
Michael Hard	Polytechnic School of Management Studies, London W.1.
Colonel Peel	Ministry of Defence.
Dick Ritchie	Lockyer & Partners Ltd., London W.1.
Bob Turner	Polytechnic School of Management Studies, London W.1.
John Sharp	Polytechnic School of Management Studies, London W.1.

and to the following organisations:

The British Broadcasting Corporation, London W.1.
Time Sharing Ltd., London W.1.
The International Labour Organisation, Geneva.
The Management Training Centre, Sofia.

CONTENTS

Contents

PREFACE

The object of this book is to give the reader a practical appreciation of Critical Path Analysis. The reader, after finishing the book, should also be able to apply the technique successfully, and develop a more sophisticated approach from experience gained during the application, and also by reference to more advanced references.

The text is aimed at a basic level, and throughout the text the points made are illustrated, where applicable, to the 'Marketing a New Product' exercise. There is also a similar exercise to be done progressively by the reader referred to as the 'Television Set'. Graded exercises are also included to ensure that the reader has grasped the pertinent points.

Included in the text are two variants on C.P.A. Activity-on-Node, which is popular on the Continent and is developing in the U.K.; and, Line of Balance, which is suited to fluctuating batch manufacturing and extends the scope of C.P.A.

The last chapters contain two full exercises which can be regarded as case studies. A complete set of answers is supplied including illustrated computer print outs.

The text has been specially developed from consultancy and teaching experience in C.P.A.

1 INTRODUCTION TO CRITICAL PATH ANALYSIS

Historical Introduction

Over the past years there has been a growing need for more effective planning and control of projects within the private and public sectors. As government and industry are continually engaged on tasks of increasing complexity the need for a systematic approach to planning and control is essential if best use is to be made of resources.

The late 50's saw significant advances in planning techniques by teams working in the U.S., U.K., and on the Continent. All the teams were engaged in devising scheduling systems to enable projects to be completed in less time than hitherto using the same or fewer resources. This meant that a technique had to be established which achieved a better integration of resources. Unfortunately all the teams were working in parallel and hence each technique developed had its own characteristics. Most of the publicity for the early work has gone to the U.S. E. I. du Pont de Nemours, who, aided by the Rand Corporation, developed Critical Path Method for controlling the construction and maintenance of chemical plant. The U.S. Navy, aided by Booz, Allen, and Hamilton, developed Program Evaluation and Review Technique (P.E.R.T.) for controlling the construction of the Polaris Missile Programme. In France Professor B. Roy was concerned with 'Graphes et Ordonnacements' (Networks and Scheduling). In the U.K. one of the first successful applications was carried out by The Central Electricity Generating Board after their operational research team produced a system which they applied in 1958 to plan and control the maintenance overhaul of Keadby Power Station. This resulted in a reduction in time of 40%.

All the systems were essentially the same and, unless specifically referred to, are in the text referred to as Critical Path Analysis which is the popular U.K. term. The early 60's saw a rapid expansion in the use of C.P.A. for 4 main reasons:

(a) Savings attributed to the initial applications.
(b) C.P.A. satisfied a demand for a more effective approach to planning both in large and small scale operations.
(c) The technique, once mastered, is remarkably simple.
(d) The technique lends itself to computers.

The reader might suspect that reasons (c) and (d) are in conflict, but this is not the case. A computer can be used in cases where manual computation becomes uneconomic.

The Use and Importance of Critical Path Analysis
C.P.A. is the organised application of systematic reasoning for planning, scheduling, and controlling practical situations where many separate jobs, which make up the whole task, can happen simultaneously, almost simultaneously or in sequence such that it is difficult intuitively to establish the relationship between the separate jobs.

C.P.A. identifies three separate phases:
(a) 'Planning Phase'. This concentrates on getting the logic of the separate jobs into the correct parallel and series sequence.
(b) 'Scheduling Phase'. This develops from the 'Planning Phase' and converts the plan into a

feasible and implementable schedule having analysed the plan with reference to optimum use of available resources, e.g. time, manpower, and equipment.

(c) 'Control Phase'. This develops from the 'Scheduling Phase' and allows actual progress to be monitored and corrections made to ensure adherence to the schedule or modified schedule.

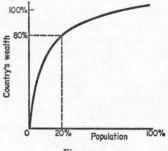

Figure 1.1

A slight digression is needed to explain the importance of C.P.A. to management. The nineteenth century economist, Vilfredo Pareto, is credited with making the obvious but very significant statement about the distribution of the country's wealth. He stated that approximately 20% of the population account for 80% of the country's wealth. Graphically the complete analysis is shown in Fig. 1.1 and this distribution is known as the 'Pareto Curve'.

It is still true today though the wealth is held by a different population. However, most important is the generalisation that in many situations a 'few occurrences' account for a 'large effect', e.g. a small proportion of employees account for most of a company's absenteeism; a small proportion of employees account for most of the company's industrial accidents, etc. Similarly, in a planning situation a small subsection of the plan will account for a large part of the total effect of the plan. C.P.A. is a powerful management diagnostic weapon which pinpoints the important small subsection, and refers to it as the 'critical path'. It is the time taken by this small subsection which determines total project time, other parts of the plan have differing amounts of surplus time.

Management should identify the important small subsection of a plan and focus most of its attention on it, and conversely need pay less attention to the rest of the plan. Note that the rest of the plan must receive some attention as it is the whole plan that matters in the long run.

It was doing precisely what has been stated that facilitated the significant reductions in time in the early applications of C.P.A. to plant maintenance scheduling and the Polaris missile construction programme. However, the Pyramids were probably built using some technique similar to C.P.A.!

2 THE ARROW DIAGRAM

The Convention

When one is considering embarking on a project, a whole host of questions arise ranging from, "How long will the project take?" to "What shall be the first job?" In C.P.A. many questions are asked in a systematic manner and the plan is gradually built up. The first stage in C.P.A. is the 'planning phase' in which an 'arrow diagram' is constructed using a set of conventions. The arrow diagram is a graphical method of specifying the order in which the various jobs, which make up the complete project, are to be carried out.

C.P.A., in common with other planning techniques, requires the project to be broken down into separate identifiable jobs, usually referred to as 'activities'. Activities are represented by 'arrows' e.g. ———→.

Each activity must have a recognisable start and finish and they are represented by 'circles' e.g. O, and are referred to as 'events' (or 'nodes').

No reference is made in the planning phase to time, and arrows are not drawn to a time scale. However the direction of the arrow is important, the 'tail' of an arrow being the start of the activity, and the 'head' of the arrow the finish. Each arrow has an associated start and finish event, and hence these are referred to as 'tail events' and 'head events'. An event is usually numbered, for identification purposes and subsequent analysis, and represents an instant in time. The symbolic representation of the task 'dig hole' would be as shown in Figure 2.1.

Event number 1 is the tail event and event number 2 is the head event. Another form of symbolic representation would be to define the task 'dig hole' as shown in Figure 2.2.

Figure 2.1 is said to be 'activity orientated', and Figure 2.2 is said to be 'event orientated'. Figure 2.1 is the original symbolic notation of Critical Path Method and Fig. 2.2 is the original symbolic notation of Program Evaluation and Review Technique. Figure 2.1 is the most common notation and will be used throughout the text. An interesting version of C.P.A. lets the

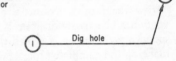

or

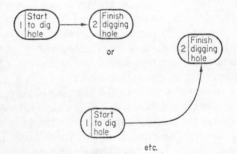

Figure 2.1

or

etc.

Figure 2.2

circle represent the activity, and the arrow represents the dependency. This is referred to as 'Activity on Node' and is described in Chapter 10.

Drawing and the Arrow Diagram

The first stage in C.P.A. is to understand the project and split it into definable and identifiable activities.

The full construction of an arrow diagram is best explained by referring to the 'Marketing a new product' example which will be developed throughout subsequent chapters.

"A sales company, trading country-wide in polishing and cleaning materials, sold mainly to industrial outlets, has been approached by a small but vigorous manufacturing concern who believe that they have succeeded in developing a revolutionary car polish, yet lack the finance and marketing experience to exploit it. Market research has validated their claim and has indicated the size of a sales force and likely expenditure on initial promotion required to capture an attractive share of the market over the next two years. In the early stages, the Sales Director will have to plan the following activities which are listed with a brief comment on policy. Trial samples are available.

Engage Sales Manager	Engage an experienced sales manager, an office is available.
Negotiate Price	The sales director will deal direct with the supplier.
Engage Salesmen	The sales manager will recruit the number indicated by market research.
Train Salesmen	Train new recruits to sell to the distributors.
Select Distributors	The sales manager will do this himself.
Approve Package Design	The sales manager will do this himself.
Package Product	The supplier will start production after agreement on price and design of package.

Obtain Orders from Distributors	Orders received from selected distributors after calls from salesmen.
Deliver Stock to Warehouse	The supplier will dispatch batches on completion of production.
Transport Stock to Distributors	This will take place from warehouse. The amount will depend on the orders received from the distributors.
Arrange Sales Promotion	The sales manager will do this, but the expenditure on promotion will depend on the price of the goods, and type of package."

The first stage in drawing the network is to list the activities, and the second stage is to arrange them in logical order using a symbolic notation.

Five questions must be asked for each activity when drawing the arrow diagram:

(1) Is this a start activity?
(2) Is this a finish activity?
(3) What activity, if any, immediately precedes this activity?
(4) What activity, if any, immediately follows this activity?
(5) What activity, if any, is concurrent with this activity?

Hence in the example a search is made for the start activity. It will be noted that in this case two activities can start concurrently, 'Engage Sales Manager' and 'Negotiate Price'. These two activities are performed by the sales director and, since the arrow diagram must start with a single event, the logic develops:

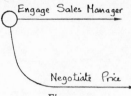

Figure 2.3

Until the completion of the arrow diagram, questions (1) to (5) must be asked over and over again. Patience, pencil, pencil sharpener, and a large rubber are essential.

Consider the activities that immediately follow 'Engage Sales Manager'. A search indicates that the sales manager *could* 'Engage Salesmen', 'Select Distributors', and 'Approve Package Design'.

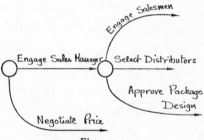

Figure 2.4

So far so good; but, what activities follow on from 'Negotiate Price'? Another search indicates 'Package Product' and 'Arrange Sales Promotion'. Hence the arrow diagram begins to spread out. (See Figure 2.5.)

Continuing the cross examination two points emerge, 'Arrange Sales Promotion' has no follow on activity and hence its head event must be the finish of the project; and 'Package Product' and 'Arrange Sales

9

Promotion' cannot take place until the activities 'Negotiate Price' and 'Approve Package Design' have been completed.

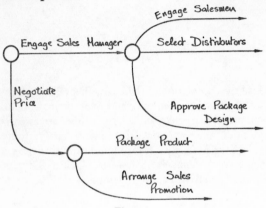

Figure 2.5

A redraft will then look like

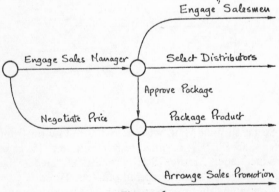

Figure 2.6

Further links in the chain are now developed. Before activity 'Obtain Orders from Distributors' can begin the activities 'Select Distributors' and 'Train Salesmen' must have been completed. A draft will look like

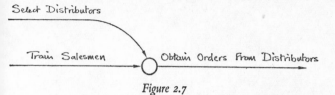

Figure 2.7

Two activities 'Deliver Stock to Warehouse' and 'Transport Stock to Distributors' have yet to be interlinked. 'Package Product' will precede 'Deliver Stock to Warehouse'. 'Transport Stock to Distributors' will follow on from the completion of 'Obtain Orders from Distributors' and 'Deliver Stock to Warehouse', producing a draft like

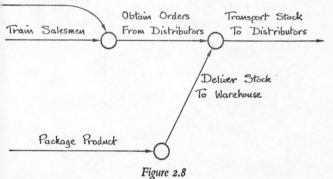

Figure 2.8

A further check reveals that 'Transport Stock to Distributors' has no follow on activity hence its head event will be common with the head event of 'Arrange Sales Promotion', and this event is the terminal event of the arrow diagram. 'Train Salesmen' must follow 'Engage Salesmen'. The centipede-like drafts, Figures

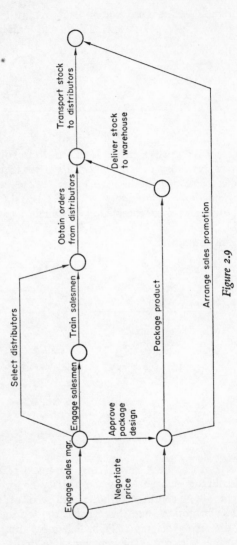

Marketing a new product

Figure 2.9

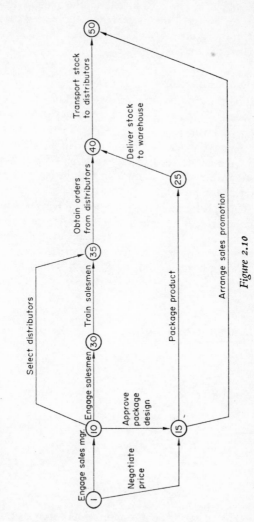

Marketing a new product

Figure 2.10

2.6 and 2.8, can now be linked up, the logic rechecked, and the arrow diagram redrafted for presentation as shown by Figure 2.9. The large rubber, now somewhat smaller, can now be discarded.

Event Numbering

Figure 2.10 shows the arrow diagram with event numbers. Numbering follows a two step convention:

(1) Number events in ascending order, beginning with the start event, and move in the direction of the arrow such that the activity's head event is always greater in number than its tail event.

(2) Leave gaps in the numbering sequence.

Step (1) is for reference purposes and future analytical reasons. It does not mean that event 25 occurs before event 35 as no reference has yet been made to time.

Step (2) is advisable to give additional flexibility, and facilitates the addition of additional activities.

e.g.

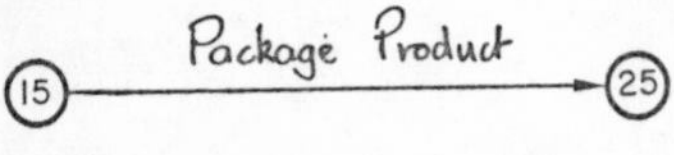

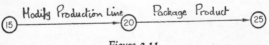

could become

Figure 2.11

Event 20 could be any number between 15 and 25 not already displayed in the arrow diagram.

Tabular Display

Arrow diagrams are frequently referred to as networks, and Network Analysis is almost as popular a term as Critical Path Analysis. To facilitate subsequent analysis and to meet the requirements of computers, arrow diagrams are often expressed in tabular form. Inspection of the network, Figure 2.10, will show that each activity can be expressed by reference to its tail and head event number. 'Engage Salesmen' has tail event 10 and head event 30, similarly 'Train Salesmen' has tail event 30

Activity Description	Code
Engage Sales Manager	1–10
Negotiate Price	1–15
Approve Package Design	10–15
Engage Salesmen	10–30
Select Distributors	10–35
Package Product	15–25
Arrange Sales Promotion	15–50
Deliver Stock to Warehouse	25–40
Train Salesmen	30–35
Obtain Orders from Distributors	35–40
Transport Stock to Distributors	40–50

Table 2.1

and head event 35. Hence a table can be built up as shown in Table 2.1 showing activities and their subsequent code. It will be noted that each activity has a unique code. In the tabulation the convention used is to list activities in order of ascending tail number. Where the activities have the same tail event then they should be listed in order of ascending head number.

Sometimes abbreviated descriptions of activities are employed when using computers, as only a portion of the computer printout can be reserved for the activity list. Most computer programs allow for up to 25 characters per description of each activity. Computers tend to have their own jargon and 'tail events' are referred to as 'i nodes' and 'head events' are referred to as 'j nodes'. Inspection will show that Table 2.1 is another way of expressing the network shown in Figure 2.10. Both displays are completely compatible, and show the relationship between activities. However, the tabular display follows on from drawing the network.

Size of Networks

Networks can be of any size, but in the first instance they should be kept simple and, perhaps, only approximate in logic because any activity chosen must be identifiable and subsequently controllable. Later chapters will show how to refine and link up networks. An approximate ground rule often given is that individual activities should be approximately 1% of the project duration, e.g. if a project lasts 2 years, activities of only 2 weeks and upwards should be considered.

Advantages of the Arrow Diagram

(1) It aids problem definition, and provides a disciplined basis for determining the constituents of a project.
(2) Agreement from different participants in a project must have been obtained to draw the network, resulting in better co-ordination.
(3) A clear picture is produced in symbolic form that ties together the activities and the managers involved.
(4) It facilitates communication because it is concise, and can be an aid in explaining projects and training personnel engaged in the project.
(5) It improves client/customer relationships.
(6) The detailed analysis often shows up inadequate methods.

Summary for Drawing the Arrow Diagram

Information Requirement:
(1) List of identifiable activities.

(2) A knowledge of the project.

Compilation of Diagram Conventions:

(1) All activities represented by arrows, the length being unimportant. By convention, time flows from tail of arrow to head of arrow.
(2) Events are instances in time and are either the start of an activity (tail event) or the finish of an activity (head event).
(3) Single start event.
(4) Single finish event.
(5) Ignore time and assume any required resources are available.
(6) Draw diagram logically asking these five questions:
    (i) Is this a start activity?
    (ii) Is this a finish activity?
    (iii) What activity, if any, immediately precedes this activity?
    (iv) What activity, if any, immediately follows this activity?
    (v) What activity, if any, is concurrent with this activity?
(7) Recheck diagram.
(8) Number events in ascending order leaving gaps.

Exercises

1. Draw the arrow diagram for 'Mailing a Letter' which has the following activities:

Write Letter
Put in Envelope
Address and Stamp Letter
Post Letter

2. Add the additional activities 'Obtain Stamp' and 'Obtain Envelope' to the network developed in Question 1.

3. Draw the arrow diagram for 'Writing a Book' which has the following activities:

Agree Title with Publisher
Prepare Draft
Type Manuscript
Check Typescript
Draft Drawings
Check Drafted Drawings
Collate Typescript and Drawings
Send to Publisher

4. Draw the arrow diagram for 'Putting on a Play' which has the following activities:

Decide on Play
Print Tickets
Sell Tickets
Issue Scripts to Cast
Cast Read Over Scripts
Rehearsals
Dress Rehearsal
Obtain Props (prior to rehearsals)
Make Costumes

5. Draw the arrow diagram for 'The Television Set'. A new model is being introduced and the following activities make up the project:

Order Electrical Components
Receive Electrical Components
Order Cabinets
Receive Cabinets
Order Packing Materials
Receive Packing Materials
Modify Production Line
Modify Test Equipment
Assemble T.V. Sets

Test T.V. Sets
Pack T.V. Sets

6. What is wrong with the following part of a network?

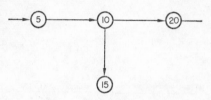

Figure 2.12

7. What is wrong with the following part of a network?

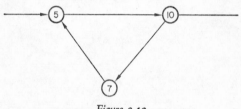

Figure 2.13

Answers to Exercises

1. and 2. See Figure 2.14.
3. See Figure 2.16.
4. See Figure 2.15.
5. See Figure 2.17.

6. This situation is referred to as 'dangling'. Activity 10–15 stops in 'mid air'. This condition violates the single event start, single event finish rule.

7. This situation is referred to as 'looping'. It is an illogical situation. 10–7 follows 5–10 which cannot

begin until 5–7 is completed, but 10–7 cannot start until 5–10 is finished! This is impossible.

Note that in answers to questions 1 to 5 any event numbering system in ascending order is acceptable.

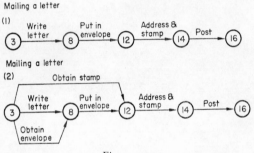

Figure 2.14

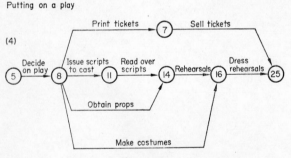

Figure 2.15

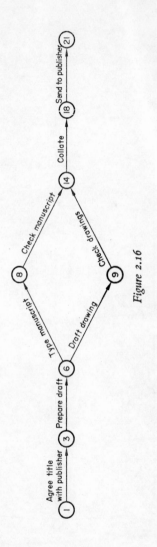

Writing a book

Figure 2.16

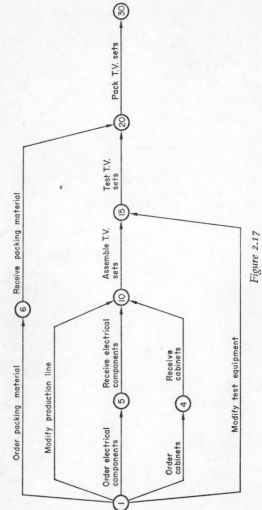

Figure 2.17

3 PROJECT DURATION AND THE CRITICAL PATH

Time Estimates

The network developed in the previous chapter can be regarded as a statement of policy. However, to prepare a schedule it is necessary to know the duration of the activities, and these are entered into the network as shown in Figure 3.1. Difficulty may be experienced in obtaining activity durations but absolute precision is not necessary. Often, on asking for durations, the answer will be preceded by a statement like, "It all depends on the weather" or other similar remarks. However an estimate must be obtained. It is worth noting the success that the U.S. Navy had using Program Evaluation and Review Technique (P.E.R.T.) which they evolved to schedule and control the Polaris Programme. In this case no one had ever built a Polaris Submarine before, but estimates were achieved for the many different activities.

P.E.R.T. differs from C.P.A. in that it requires three estimates for each activity, e.g.

> Quickest reasonable time
> Most likely time
> Worst time

The duration for each activity is taken

$$= \frac{\text{Worst} + 4\,(\text{Most likely}) + \text{Quickest}}{6}.$$

P.E.R.T. is based on statistics to allow for uncertainty and, although found useful in the U.S., is rarely used in

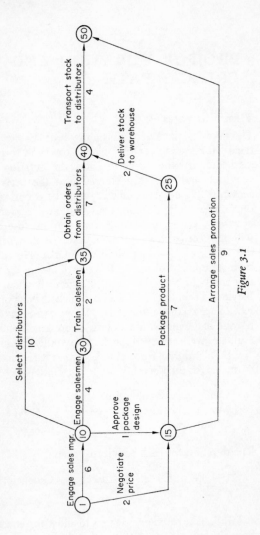

Marketing a new product

Figure 3.1

the U.K. or on the Continent. However, the idea of asking for three estimates is useful as it serves to break the ice when dealing with people who are reluctant to give estimates even though one's intention is only to use the most likely time. It is surprising how many reluctant people there are around!

Forward Pass for Project Duration

The project duration can be calculated by taking any reference point in time but, for convenience, the

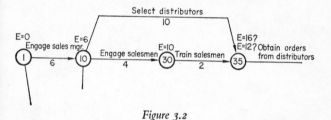

Figure 3.2

reference point is usually taken as zero. To determine the project duration, the 'earliest time' at which events can take place is considered. The 'earliest time' is designated by the letter 'E', and for the start event, in this case event number 1, 'E = 0'. Proceeding along the direction of the arrows, the 'earliest time' event 10 can occur will be the 'earliest start time' plus the duration, hence E = 6. The 'earliest time' for an event is the 'earliest time' for the preceding event plus the corresponding activity duration.

However, if this rule is applied to events 30 and 35, event 35 would appear to have two 'earliest times'; but, by definition there can be only one 'earliest time'. Reference to Figure 3.2 shows that 'Obtain Orders from Distributors' cannot begin until the completion of 'Train Salesmen' and 'Select Distributors'; hence the 'earliest time' that 'Obtain Orders from Distributors'

25

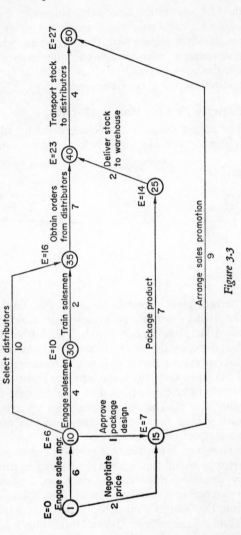

Figure 3-3

Critical Path Analysis

Marketing a new product

Engage sales mgr. 6 · Negotiate price 2 · Approve package design 1 · Engage salesmen 4 · Select distributors 10 · Train salesmen 2 · Obtain orders from distributors 7 · Package product 7 · Deliver stock to warehouse 2 · Transport stock to distributors 4 · Arrange sales promotion 9

E=0 · E=6 · E=7 · E=10 · E=16 · E=14 · E=23 · E=27

can commence is 'E = 16'. Where there is a choice the highest value is taken. The number of values will equal the number of activities terminating at that event.

The rule for the Forward Pass to determine the project duration is now:

(1) Start with the start event and let 'E = 0'.
(2) The 'earliest time' for the succeeding event is the 'earliest time' for the preceding event plus the corresponding activity duration.
(3) If, at an event, there appear to be two or more 'earliest times' choose the highest, and proceed as in step 2.

The complete forward pass is shown in Figure 3.3, and hence the 'earliest time' that event 50 can be reached is 27 weeks—the project duration.

Backward Pass for the Critical Path

Investigation in Figure 3.2 will show that 'Train Salesmen' could expand by four (days) without upsetting the start of 'Obtain Orders from Distributors'. This leeway in the subsequent schedule is referred to as float and is dealt with in Chapter 6. However, in any network there will be a chain of activities in which there is no leeway or float. The effect is similar to a convoy in which the voyage duration depends on the speed of the slowest ship. The Backward Pass enables one to determine in which chain of activities there is no float. This chain of activities is known as the 'critical path'. In the Backward Pass one is concerned with the 'latest time' at which an event can occur without delaying the completion date of the total project, and this is designated by the letter 'L'.

The 'earliest finish', if accepted as a viable date, is also equal to the latest possible completion date of the project. The 'latest time' that event 50 can occur is therefore 27 weeks. The 'latest time' that event 40 can

Critical Path Analysis

occur will be the 'latest time' for event 50 minus the activity duration. Hence for event 40, 'L = 23'.

The 'latest time' that event 25 can occur will be the 'latest time' for event 40 minus the duration of 'Deliver Stock to Warehouse'. Hence, as before, L = 25 for event 25. In general the 'latest time' for an event is the

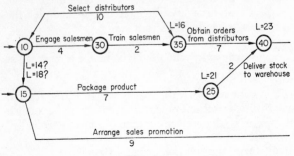

Figure 3.4

'latest time' of the succeeding event minus the corresponding duration. In the Backward Pass one starts with the last event and continues along the network going against the arrow heads. Reference to Figure 3.4 shows that at event 15 there appear two 'latest times', but, by inference there can only be one 'latest time'—the question is which one? The 'latest time', L = 18, is due to 'Arrange Sales Promotion': and the 'latest time', L = 14, is due to 'Package Product'. The two activities in question are shown in Figure 3.5 on a time scale.

If 'Package Product' starts any later than week 14 the project will not be completed by the already agreed finish. However, 'Arrange Sales Promotion' can be brought forward to week 14 without delaying the project. Hence the choice of a unique 'latest time' is taken as L = 14. The situation is the reverse of that which was found when dealing with the Forward Pass; hence, where there is a choice, the lowest value is taken. The number of alternative values will equal the number of activities leaving that event.

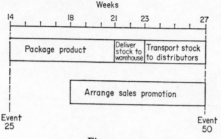

Figure 3.5

The rule for the Backward Pass to determine the Critical Path is now:

(1) Start with the last event and make the 'latest event time' = Project Duration.

(2) The 'latest time' for an event is the 'latest time' of the succeeding event minus the corresponding duration.

(3) If, at an event there appear to be two or more 'latest times', choose the lowest and proceed as in step 2.

The complete Backward Pass is shown in Figure 3.6 and the Critical Path, Figure 3.7, is 1–10–35–40–50. At events 1, 10, 35, 40 and 50 the 'earliest times' and 'latest times' are equal. When this is the case there is said to be no 'event slack'. Event slack is the difference between the 'earliest time' and the 'latest time' for a particular event. The event slack for event 25 is $21 - 14 = 7$ weeks. This means that that 'Package Product' can finish and 'Deliver Stock to Warehouse' can begin in any of the 7 weeks commencing from week 14 without delay to the project. Where there is no slack, activities

29

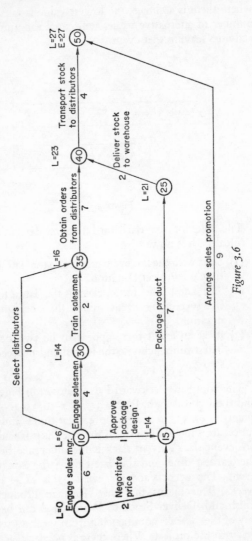

Marketing a new product

Figure 3.6

Marketing a new product

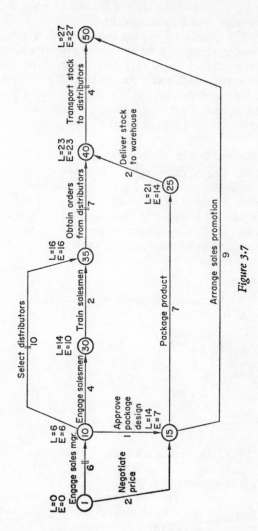

Figure 3.7

must start and finish at fixed events, and hence these are referred to as critical activities.

It is worthwhile noting that the project duration is only as accurate as the sum of the original estimates of each activity, and it may be necessary to recheck the estimates which are on the critical path. However, note how effective C.P.A. is becoming as it is already a time-saver, in as much as only the critical activities, and near critical activities, need be checked or refined.

Method Study

If the project duration is too long and it is necessary to shrink the project time, the only immediately effective time reduction will be made on the critical path. Hence it may be necessary to apply method study, and other cost reduction techniques on the critical activities. The implications of shrinking the critical path are developed in subsequent chapters.

Exercises

1. Determine the project duration and the critical path for:

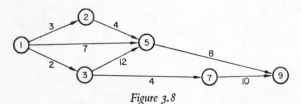

Figure 3.8

What is the event slack at event 5 and event 7?

2. Is the critical path the chain of activities through the events with zero slack?

3. Analyse 'The Television Set' for the project duration and the critical path if the activities have the following durations:

Order Electrical Components	4 weeks
Receive Electrical Components	4
Order Cabinets	4
Receive Cabinets	2
Order Packing Materials	4
Receive Packing Materials	6
Modify Production Line	4
Modify Test Equipment	6
Assemble T.V. Sets	4
Test T.V. Sets	2
Pack T.V. Sets	2

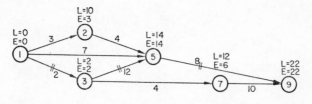

Figure 3.9

Answers to Exercises

1. The critical path is shown as —‖—. The project duration is 22 days.
Event slack at event 5 is 14 — 14 = 0.
Event slack at event 7 is 12 — 6 = 6.

2. No. If this were the case activity 1-5 would be a critical activity. One has to be careful using the concept of zero event slack to define the critical path. The critical path does run through events of zero slack but certain non-critical paths also run through events with zero slack.

3. See Figure 3.10.
Project duration 16 weeks.
Critical path —‖—.

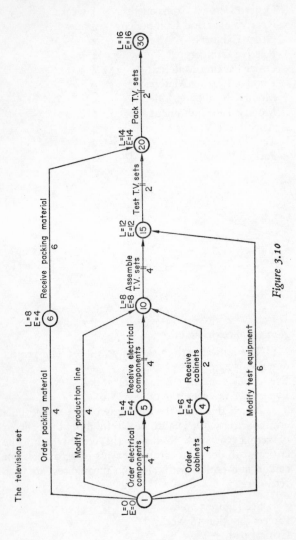

The television set

Figure 3.10

4 TABULAR ANALYSIS

List of Activities and Durations

As stated in Chapter 2 an alternative to the arrow diagram is the tabular display. To the list of activities, defined by head and tail events, is now added associated durations as shown in Table 4.1.

Activity	Code	Duration (Weeks)
Engage Sales Manager	1–10	6
Negotiate Price	1–15	2
Approve Package Design	10–15	1
Engage Salesmen	10–30	4
Select Distributors	10–35	10
Package Product	15–25	7
Arrange Sales Promotion	15–50	9
Deliver Stock to Warehouse	25–40	2
Train Salesmen	30–35	2
Obtain Order from Distributors	35–40	7
Transport Stock to Distributors	40–50	4

Table 4.1

The network in this form is suitable for computer or manual analysis. Tabular analysis is an additional and much used refinement to the analysis carried out in Chapter 3. In Chapter 3 the analysis was conducted by considering event starts and finishes—in other words was 'event orientated'. In the tabular analysis emphasis is placed upon the activities and is 'activity orientated'.

Tabular analysis is the most common form of computer analysis. Costs of computer analysis will vary but it is reasonable to suggest that networks up to 100/300 activities can be economically analysed by manual computation.

Starts and Finishes

Refer to the network as analysed in Chapter 3, Figure 3.7 and consider the activity 'Arrange Sales Promotion'.

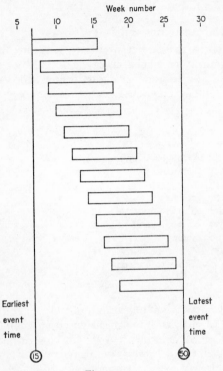

Figure 4.1

The earliest start of this activity is week 7 and if the activity starts in week 7 and has a duration of 9 weeks the earliest possible finish will be week 16. However, the project could start in week 8, 9, 10, etc. to week 18 with subsequent finishes in week 17, 18, 19, etc. to week 27. It is the object of the tabular analysis to record

36

the start and finish of each activity, but, since most activities each have differing starts and finishes the problem is which starts and finishes to record.

Another approach would be to consider that the activity 'Arrange Sales Promotion' must be finished at a latest time of week 27 if the project is not to be delayed. If the latest possible finish of the activity is 27 and the activity has a duration of 9 weeks the latest possible start would be week 18. However, the project could finish in week 26, 25, 24, etc. to week 16 with associated starts in week 17, 16, 15, etc. to week 7.

The possible starts and finishes of the activity 'Arrange Sales Promotion' drawn to a time scale are shown in Figure 4.1.

To formulate the tabular analysis only two parameters are considered:

(a) The 'earliest start' with subsequent 'earliest finish'. The first alternative shown in Figure 4.1.
(b) The 'latest finish' with precedent 'latest start'. The last alternative shown in Figure 4.1.

These two parameters expressed in tabular analysis form are shown below.

Activity	Code	Duration	Start		Finish	
			E	L	E	L
Arrange Sales Promotion	15–50	9	7	18	16	27

Table 4.2

The 'earliest start' and 'latest finish' are derived from the analysis of the arrow diagram, and are the activities earliest tail and latest head events respectively.

The 'earliest finish' and 'latest start' are computed:
(a) 'Earliest finish' = 'earliest start' + duration
(b) 'Latest start'   = 'latest finish' − duration.

The complete tabular analysis for the network is shown in Table 4.3. A useful check on the computation is that the latest start — earliest start should always equal the latest finish — earliest finish.

Float

Inspection of Table 4.3 will show that certain activities do not have any flexibility of start and finish, e.g.

'Engage Sales Manager'
'Select Distributors'
'Obtain Orders'
'Transport Stock to Distributors'

Activity	Code	Duration	Start		Finish	
			E	L	E	L
Engage Sales Manager	1–10	6	0	0	6	6
Negotiate Price	1–15	2	0	12	2	14
Approve Package Design	10–15	1	6	13	7	14
Engage Salesmen	10–30	4	6	10	10	14
Select Distributors	10–35	10	6	6	16	16
Package Product	15–25	7	7	14	14	21
Arrange Sales Promotion	15–50	9	7	18	16	27
Deliver Stock to W'House	25–40	2	14	21	16	23
Train Salesmen	30–35	2	10	14	12	16
Obtain Orders from Distributors	35–40	7	16	16	23	23
Transport Stock to Distributors	40–50	4	23	23	27	27

Table 4.3

As shown in the previous chapter these activities are on the critical path, and are referred to as critical activities.

If it is necessary to draw 'Select Distributors' to a time scale there is only one possible way, Figure 4.2, as opposed to 'Arrange Sales Promotion' as drawn in Figure 4.1.

In the case of 'Select Distributors' there are 10 weeks available to carry out a 10 week activity, while in the case of 'Arrange Sales Promotion' there is from the earliest start to the latest finish to carry out the activity; a total of 20 weeks to carry out a 9 week activity. Hence if 'Arrange Sales Promotion' starts as early as possible it could expand by 11 weeks without delaying

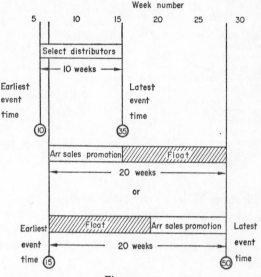

Figure 4.2

the project. Alternatively, 'Arrange Sales Promotion' could have its start delayed by 11 weeks without subsequent delay to the project duration. Figure 4.2 shows the differences.

The amount of time an activity, started at its earliest time, may expand without affecting the duration of a project is referred to as 'float'. Hence the float of activity 'Select Distributors' is nil, while activity 'Arrange Sales Promotion' has 11 weeks. The effect is shown by cross hatching. Critical activities are now redefined as having zero float. Hence all non-critical

39

activities will have float of varying magnitude. If, in relation to the total overall time certain activities have a small amount of float the activities are said to be subcritical. Activities 'Engage Salesmen' and 'Train Salesmen' form a sub-critical path.

Activity	Code	Duration	Start E	Start L	Finish E	Finish L	Float Total
Engage Sales Mgr	1–10	6	0	0	6	6	0
Negotiate Price	1–15	2	0	12	2	14	12
Approve Pkg Design	10–15	1	6	13	7	14	7
Engage Salesmen	10–30	4	6	10	10	14	4
Select Distributors	10–35	10	6	6	16	16	0
Package Product	15–25	7	7	14	14	21	7
Arr. Sales Promotion	15–50	9	7	18	16	27	11
Del. Stock to W'house	25–40	2	14	21	16	23	7
Train Salesmen	30–35	2	10	14	12	16	4
Obtain Order from Distributors	35–40	7	16	16	23	23	0
Transport Stock to Distributors	40–50	4	23	23	27	27	0

Table 4.4

Float can be derived by the formula:

TOTAL AVAILABLE TIME FOR ACTIVITY — ACTIVITY DURATION

= (LATEST FINISH — EARLIEST START) — ACTIVITY DURATION

= LATEST START — EARLIEST START *or* LATEST FINISH — EARLIEST FINISH.

Float, up till now, has been considered generally and is referred to as Total Float. Table 4.4 shows the completed tabular analysis.

Tabular Analysis by Computer

A computer will carry out the tabular analysis when fed with the data as given in Table 4.1 and will produce a printout similar to Table 4.4.

Special programs are provided by computer manufacturers for network analysis and the network programs usually require each activity, code, and duration on a punched card.

An illustration of a simple computer printout is shown in Table 4.5. Instead of week numbers actual dates are entered. Each activity is also allocated to be the

PERT PROGRAM BY TIME SHARING LTD

ACTIVITY	EVENTS	DUR.	ESTART	LSTART	EFINISH	LFINISH	FLOAT	DEPT
1	1 - 10	6	17JAN	17JAN	28FEB	28FEB	0	1
2	1 - 15	2	17JAN	11APR	31JAN	25APR	12	1
3	10 - 15	11	28FEB	18APR	7MAR	25APR	7	1
4	10 - 30	4	28FEB	28MAR	28MAR	25APR	4	1
5.	10 - 35	10	28FEB	28FEB	9MAY	9MAY	0	1
6	15 - 25	7	7MAR	25APR	25APR	13JUN	7	1
7	15 - 50	9	7MAR	23MAY	9MAY	25JUL	11	1
8	25 - 40	2	25APR	13JUN	9MAY	27JUN	7	1
9	30 - 35	2	28MAR	25APR	11 APR	9MAY	4	1
10	35 - 40	7	9MAY	9 MAY	27JUN	27JUN	0	1
11	40 - 50	4	27JUN	27JUN	25JUL	25JUL	0	1

ACTIVITY	EVENTS	DUR.	ESTART	LSTART	EFINISH	LFINISH	FLOAT	DEPT
1	1 - 10	6	17JAN	17JAN	28FEB	28FEB	0	1
5	10 - 35	10	28FEB	28FEB	9MAY	9MAY	0	1
10	35 - 40	7	9MAY	9 MAY	27JUN	27JUN	0	1
11	40 - 50	4	27JUN	27JUN	25JUL	25JUL	0	1

Table 4.5

responsibility of Department 1. Also the critical activities have been separately printed out.

Computer analysis is somewhat out of the scope of this text, but most manufacturers and computer bureaux will provide free literature on their network analysis software. More reference is made to computer analysis in subsequent chapters, and a useful summary of the facilities offered by computers is enclosed in the chapter headed "Summary of Critical Path Analysis".

Exercises

1. Draw up the tabular analysis for the network analysed in Question 1 in Chapter 3.

2. Draw up the tabular analysis for 'The Television Set' as analysed in Question 3 in Chapter 3.

Answers to Exercises

1.

Activity Code	Duration	Start		Finish		Float
		E	L	E	L	Total
1–2	3	0	7	3	10	7
1–3	2	0	0	2	2	0
1–5	7	0	7	7	14	7
2–5	4	3	10	7	14	7
3–5	12	2	2	14	14	0
3–7	4	2	8	6	12	6
5–9	8	14	14	22	22	0
7–9	10	6	12	16	22	6

Table 4.6

2.

Activity	Code	Duration	Start		Finish		Float
			E	L	E	L	Total
Order Cabinets	1–4	4	0	2	4	6	2
Order Elect. Cmpts	1–5	4	0	0	4	4	0
Order Packing Mat.	1–6	4	0	4	4	8	4
Mod. Prod. Line	1–10	4	0	4	4	8	4
Mod. Test Equipm't	1–15	6	0	6	6	12	6
Receive Cabinets	4–10	2	4	6	6	8	2
Receive Elec. Cmpts	5–10	4	4	4	8	8	0
Receive Pkg Mat.	6–20	6	4	8	10	14	4
Ass. T.V. Sets	10–15	4	8	8	12	12	0
Test T.V. Sets	15–20	2	12	12	14	14	0
Pack T.V. Sets	20–30	2	14	14	16	16	0

Table 4.7

5 BAR CHARTS AND C.P.A.

Introduction

To use successfully any of the information gleaned up to date one has to be able to communicate it. One disadvantage of the tabular analysis is that it lacks visual impact, and a knowledge of C.P.A. is required to use it successfully. A more useful presentation to show when jobs start and finish would be to draw the network to

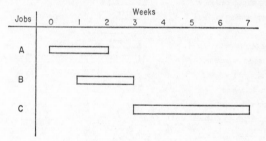

Figure 5.1

a time scale, and forget about the tabular analysis; however, networks have poor aesthetic appeal and look even odder when drawn to a time scale. Also the problem arises as to how to draw an activity to scale when it has a choice of starts with associated resultant finishes. It is only rarely that networks are drawn to scale as they are essentially planning devices, and not analysing devices.

Bar Charts

The conventional method of planning and scheduling work is to use the bar chart (or the more specialised

Gantt chart[1] format), in which the activities are listed and the associated activity time is shown by a line drawn to scale representing 100% of the job.

Figure 5.1 indicates that job, or activity A, is planned to start at week 0 and is planned to take 2 weeks, activity B is planned to start at week 1 and is planned to take 2 weeks, and that activity C is planned to start at week 3 and is planned to take 4 weeks.

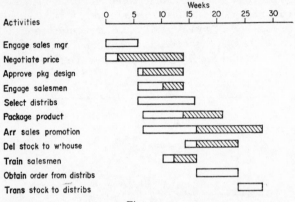

Figure 5.2

The relationship between the jobs is shown, but if an attempt is made to use bar charts straight off on a complex project, it is difficult to establish the exact inter-relationships. However, since bar charts are readily understood and facilitate monitoring of progress, it is reasonable to convert the network into a bar chart using the analysed network or the tabular analysis. Initially, the problem of variable starts is overcome by showing all activities starting at their earliest start and finishing at their earliest finish. The amount of float is

[1] A useful chapter on Gantt Charting is in the *Industrial Engineering Handbook*, edited by H. B. Maynard, published by McGraw-Hill.

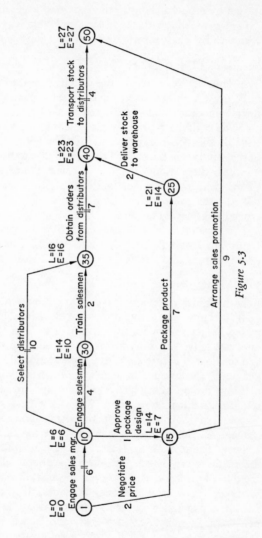

Marketing a new product

Figure 5-3

shown by cross-hatching to the activities' latest finish.

Figure 5.2 shows the network (in Figure 5.3) converted to bar chart form.

Sequenced Gantt Chart

The dependencies between the activities is not shown in Figure 5.2, and to overcome this the bar chart can be further modified and represented as shown in Figure 5.4. The critical activities are placed along the top line, and the other activities appear in parallels. The grouping of the activities in the parallel chain is similar to the way in which the activities form branches in the network. In this way the inter-relationships can be shown by dotted lines, and the chart cross referenced to the network by displaying event numbers.

This type of chart is often referred to as a Sequenced Gantt Chart or a Barrow Diagram (because it is composed of 'bars' and 'arrows').

Free Float

In both Figures 5.2 and 5.4 it is easy to grasp the concept of float. However, if the amount of float is added up in Figure 5.2 and in Figure 5.4 it will be seen that it does not tally. The float in Figure 5.2 adds up to 52, and the float in Figure 5.4 adds up to 27! Float has been defined as the amount an activity can expand without delaying the project. This definition is still true but it requires careful interpretation. Refer to Figure 5.2 or Table 4.4 in Chapter 4 and note that the float on activity 'Engage Salesmen' is 4 weeks and that the float on activity 'Train Salesmen' is also 4 weeks. In either case each activity can expand by 4 weeks without delaying the overall project date. However, this float of 4 weeks is shared between these two activities. If 'Engage Salesmen' expands by 2 weeks this will delay the start of 'Train Salesmen' by 2 weeks, and hence 'Train Salesmen' could only expand by 2 weeks if the overall

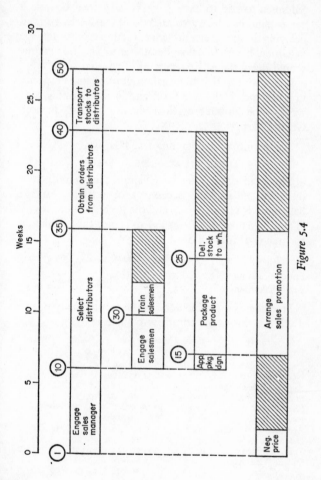

Figure 5.4

project time is not to be delayed. This effect is readily seen when referring to Figure 5.4. The activity 'Train Salesmen' is said to have 4 weeks 'free float' because it can expand in a forwards direction by 4 weeks without delaying the start of any subsequent activity. Note 'Engage Salesmen' has no free float because any expansion in time would delay the earliest start of 'Train Salesmen'.

It can be seen that the total amount of spare capacity in a network is the free float, and in the example is 27 weeks—the amount of float shown by a Sequenced Gnatt Chart.

The formula for obtaining free float is

TOTAL FLOAT — HEAD SLACK

The head slack (refer to Chapter 3 to refresh your memory on slack if necessary) of activity 'Engage Salesmen' is $14 - 10 = 4$, and the head slack of activity 'Train Salesmen' is $16 - 16 = 0$. Hence the calculation for free float is as follows:

Activity	Total Float	Head Slack	Free Float
Engage Salesmen	4	4	$4 - 4 = 0$
Train Salesmen	4	0	$4 - 0 = 4$

Free float is often included in the tabular analysis, and Table 5.1 shows the complete tabular analysis.

Activity	Code	Duration	Start E	Start L	Finish E	Finish L	T	F	I
Engage Sales Mgr	1–10	6	0	0	6	6	0	0	0
Negotiate Price	1–15	2	0	12	2	14	12	5	5
Approve Pkg Design	10–15	1	6	13	7	14	7	0	0
Engage Salesmen	10–30	4	6	10	10	14	4	0	0
Select Distributors	10–35	10	6	6	16	16	0	0	0
Package Product	15–25	7	7	14	14	21	7	0	0
Arr. Sales Promotion	15–50	9	7	18	16	27	11	11	4
Del. Stock to W'house	25–40	2	14	21	16	23	7	7	0
Train Salesmen	30–35	2	10	14	12	16	4	4	0
Obtain Order from Distributors	35–40	7	16	16	23	23	0	0	0
Transport Stock to Distributors	40–50	4	23	23	27	27	0	0	0

Table 5.1

It will be noticed that activity 'Negotiate Price' has a total float of 12 weeks, and of this, 5 weeks is free float. Reference to Figure 5.3 will show that 'Negotiate Price' can expand by 5 weeks without delaying the start of either 'Package Product' or 'Arrange Sales Promotion'.

Another type of float exists called 'independent float' which is mentioned for the record only as it seems to have a fairly restricted use, but is common on computer printouts. Consider the activity 'Arrange Sales Promotion' and note that it cannot start until the completion of activities 'Approve Package Design' and 'Negotiate Price'. If the activities 'Approve Package Design' and 'Negotiate Price' consume all their available float their latest finish date will be week 14, but activity 'Arrange Sales Promotion' need not start until week 18. Hence activity 'Arrange Sales Promotion' is said to have $18 - 14 = 4$ weeks independent float.

In general an activity is said to have independent float if all its preceding activities have consumed all their available float and there is still float within the activity. Table 5.1 also shows the independent float for the network

The calculation for independent float is as follows:

Free Float — Tail Slack

Activity	Free Float	Tail Slack	Independent Float
Approve Package Design	0	0	$0 - 0 = 0$
Arrange Sales Promotion	11	7	$11 - 7 = 4$

Summary of Float

Total Float is the amount an activity can expand without affecting the overall duration of a project.

Free Float is the amount an activity can expand without affecting the succeeding activity.

Independent Float is the amount an activity can expand without affecting the preceding activity or the succeeding activity.

Illustrated example of Total, Free, and Independent Float.

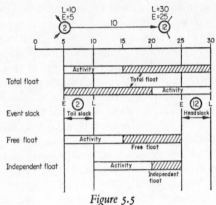

Figure 5.5

Computers—Bar Charts and Float

Computers can print out bar charts, but not in sequenced form. As with the tabular analysis, the input data required is activity, code, and duration. The manner of

```
TIME SHARING LTD                        PERT PROGRAM

PROJECT                                 MARKETING A NEW PRODUCT

ACTIVITY              Ø    5   10   15   20   25   30

ENGAGE SALES MGR      CCCCCC

NEG PRICE             XX*****------*

APP PKG DESIGN        X-------

ENGAGE SALESMEN       XXXX----

SELECT DISTRIBS       CCCCCCCCCC

PACKAGE PRODUCT            XXXXXXX-------

ARR SALES PROMOTION       XXXXXXXXX************

DEL STOCK TO W'HOUSE           XX*******

TRAIN SALESMEN            XX****

OBT ORD FROM DISTRIBS          CCCCCCC

TRANS STOCK TO DISTRIBS              CCCC
```

Table 5.2

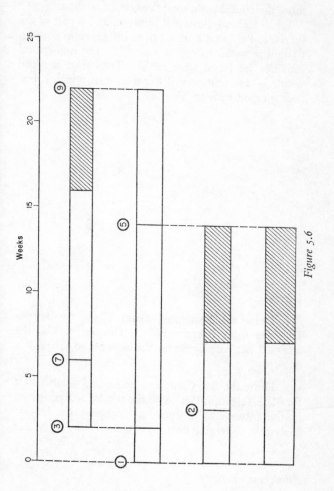

Figure 5.6

printout varies but there is incorporated a facility to show the critical path, total float, and free float.

Table 5.2 is an illustrated printout, and is part of the P.E.R.T. PROGRAM referred to in the previous chapter. Critical activities are typed with a 'C', and non-critical activities are typed with an 'A'. Total float is typed with a '-' and that part of the total float which is free float is typed with an '*'.

Exercises

1. Draw the Sequenced Gantt Chart or Barrow Diagram from Exercise No. 1, Chapter 3. Use the analysed network given in the answers to Chapter 3 only.

2. Draw the Bar Chart and Sequenced Gantt Chart for 'The Television Set'. Use the tabular analysis given in the answers to Chapter 4. Complete the tabular analysis to show free float.

Answers to Exercises

1. See Figure 5.6.

2. See Figures 5.7 and 5.8.

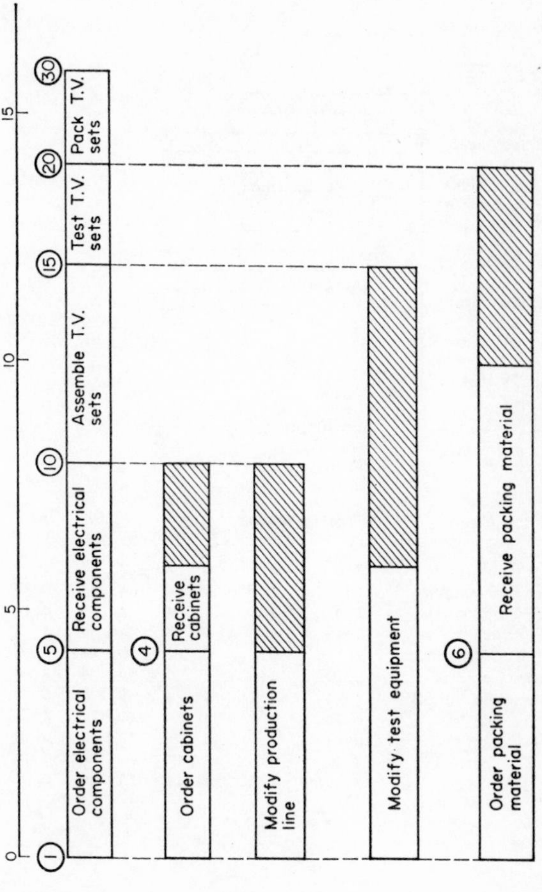
0
5
10
15
1
5
10
15
20
30
4
6
Order electrical components
Receive electrical components
Assemble T.V. sets
Test T.V. sets
Pack T.V. sets
Order cabinets
Receive cabinets
Modify production line
Modify test equipment
Order packing material
Receive packing material

Figure 5.7

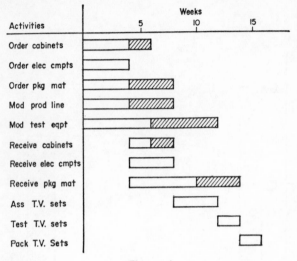

Figure 5.8

Activity	Code	Duration	Start E	L	Finish E	L	Float T	F
Order Cabinets	1–4	4	0	2	4	6	2	0
Order Elec. Cmpts	1–5	4	0	0	4	4	0	0
Order Pkg Material	1–6	4	0	4	4	8	4	0
Mod. Prod Line	1–10	4	0	4	4	8	4	4
Mod. Test Equipm't	1–15	6	0	6	6	12	6	6
Receive Cabinets	4–10	2	4	6	6	8	2	2
Receive Elec Cmpts	5–10	4	4	4	8	8	0	0
Receive Pkg Mat.	6–20	6	4	8	10	14	4	4
Ass T.V. Sets	10–15	4	8	8	12	12	0	0
Test T.V. Sets	15–20	2	12	12	14	14	0	0
Pack T.V. Sets	20–30	2	14	14	16	16	0	0

Table 5.3

6 USE OF FLOAT

Resource Analysis

Until now only time has been considered and resources such as men, money, machines and materials have been assumed to be available in unlimited quantities. Hence, having produced a plan and analysed its effect with respect to time, one must reconcile it to fit any specified time table and to take account of available resources. This process is referred to generally as scheduling.

In the scheduling phase enormous complexities often exist when resources are applied to a network, and the network manipulated to see the effect of the different resources interacting. The possible combinations are often beyond even the power of computers, and hence good approximate answers are often sought.

Another approach is to dispense with the formalities of the resource analysis computations outlined in the next paragraphs and just make use of the float, using a bit of common sense, on the basis of the old Scottish adage that one can safely put a chameleon on a red rug or a green rug, or even a red and green rug, but the resulting problems from putting a chameleon on a tartan rug might not justify the risk.

Resource Aggregation

Graphically, resource aggregation is carried out by drawing a histogram and observing the effect of all activities starting as early as possible, or alternatively observing the effect of all activities starting as late as possible.

Consider a simple network as in Figure 6.1. Assume

that the resources are manpower and the men are completely interchangeable from one activity to another.

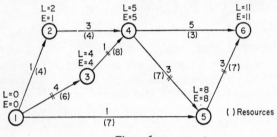

Figure 6.1

Resource aggregation is best achieved working from a Sequenced Gantt Chart. Figure 6.2 shows the Sequenced Gantt Chart for the network described by Figure 6.1. From the chart a histogram is constructed which shows the resources employed with respect to time. For example, in the first week $6 + 4 + 7 = 17$ men are employed, and this is completed week by week to obtain the complete histogram. The area under the curve represents the resources employed. The shaded area represents the resources employed on critical activities.

Resource Allocation

Assume that the maximum number of men available is 10, and display this by a resource level line. Figure 6.2 shows that resources are not used evenly and that the project cannot be completed in 10 weeks with 10 men, unless sub-contracting is considered. However, if certain activities are late started by consuming free float this will have a smoothing effect. Despite the fact that there are 9 days free float, there are many different combinations of Sequenced Gantt Charts resulting in different

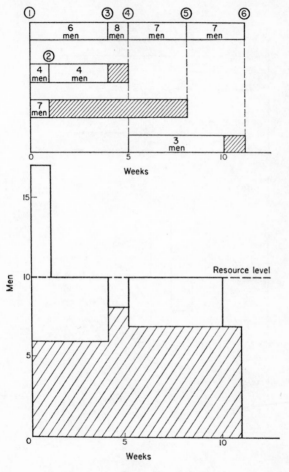

Figure 6.2

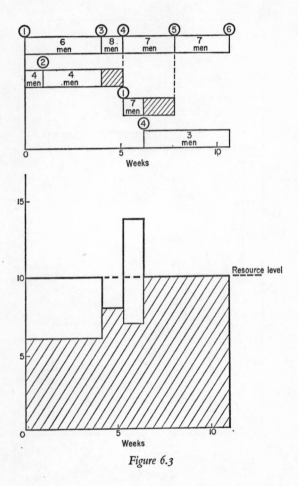

Figure 6.3

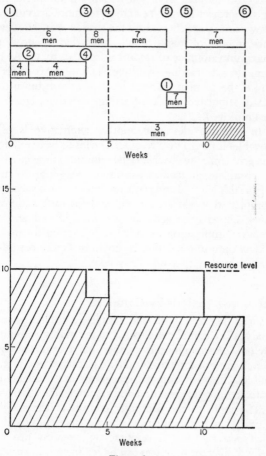

Figure 6.4

histograms. The optimum solution is shown in Figure 6.3, but, though it is an improvement, it still does not meet the resource level. The maximum number of men on the project is now 14 and, note, more activities are now critical, as reflected by the shaded area. However, the process of resource allocation has reduced the maximum number of resources from 17 to 14. At this stage sub-contracting, overtime, etc. must be considered, and if the 10 man resource level—10 week finish time is still stipulated, sub-contracting, overtime, etc. must be employed.

In resource allocation another alternative is often possible. If the 10 man resource level is to be maintained the problem now is, what is the minimum time in which to complete the contract without exceeding 10 men. Again this is a trial and error process in which successive completion weeks are chosen, and for each additional week chosen, the activities are manipulated and the resource implication recorded in histogram form.

The optimum solution is shown in Figure 6.4. Note that only activity 4-6 has any float.

Resource Analysis by Computer

As can be seen with the simple example, resource analysis is a complex business and invariably computers are used. Also, in most cases, multiple resources are used which are not interchangeable, e.g. carpenters, joiners, and plumbers. Computer programs are available for both resource aggregation and resource allocation.

The input to the computer consists of the activity, activity code, duration, and the resource employed on each activity. For a resource aggregation program several different resources can be fed in and, in addition to the tabular analysis and bar charts, resource histograms will be printed out for each resource starting as early as possible, or as late as possible.

In resource allocation programs the same input is required as in the resource aggregation program, but the maximum resources available should be stipulated. In this case the activities will be arranged so that the resources are never exceeded, and if insufficient resources are available the project completion date will be delayed. Alternatively, in a resource allocation program, the normal completion date will be adhered to and the additional resources required will be indicated. In certain cases a compromise between the two can be achieved by specifying 'threshold' resources. These are additional resources such as sub-contracting, shift working and overtime which could be made available if the project could not be completed in normal time. If the normal completion date still cannot be achieved, the completion date will be advanced so that the project will be completed consuming no more than the 'threshold' resources. The extension in time is referred to as the 'threshold' time.

Reducing the Overall Project Time

The overall duration of a project can only be shortened if the critical activities are reduced in time.

It is usually possible to reduce the project time by applying method study, and other cost reduction techniques. The cost of shrinking an activity may increase, but there will be an overall net saving to the project.

C.P.A. is a very useful technique in pinpointing the activities in which it is worth considering the application of method study. There is no advantage in applying method study to activities which have generous float.

To apply method study to an activity an established procedure is followed[1] in which critical questions are asked to establish the facts concerning the activity. The first stage in the questioning technique is to ask:

WHAT is achieved?
WHERE is it achieved?

When is it achieved?
Who achieves it?
How is it achieved?

Answers to the questions are sought to complete the presentation of the facts, and alternatives developed and pursued to determine a saving. It is not unknown for activities to appear on the critical path and be subsequently found to be unnecessary!

Brainstorming, as used in value analysis,[2] can be another useful cost reduction technique. In this case several people concerned with the project will sit around a table, and informally generate ideas with no holds barred to reduce activity time. It is found that working in a team people are often more creative than working individually. The ideas generated are then evaluated and developed.

Critical Path Method

As outlined in the previous paragraph the general, and usually most effective, method is to apply method study techniques. However another approach is now described which is referred to as Critical Path Method. The techniques of method study are generally well described in other texts, but the essential difference between C.P.M. and C.P.A. is explained in few texts and hence is elaborated here. The reader should bear in mind that C.P.M. is of limited use. It is used more extensively in the U.S. than in the U.K.

Often in shrinking a project the cost will increase because of using increased resources to achieve a reduction in activity time, e.g. working overtime, dispatching by air freight in lieu of sea transport. Reduction in project time has to be traded off against increased costs incurred in the project. Critical Path Method was developed with this concept in mind, and attempts to establish relationships between cost and time. Most activities can be approximated by the graph shown in Figure 6.5. Assume that point A is the original estimate

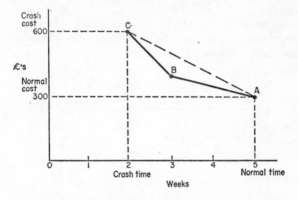

Figure 6.5

for the activity to be completed in normal time, point B represents the cost and time achieved by working overtime, and point C represents the cost and time achieved by working 2 shifts—the minimum realistic time in this case.

The associated cost and time points at A and C are referred to as 'normal' and 'crash'. It is a reasonable hypothesis to assume that to extend the activity time beyond 5 weeks will increase costs owing to insufficient use of resources, and to reduce the activity time to 1 week or less would increase costs prohibitively. The relationship between points A, B, and C, is not linear; but the relationship can be approximated by a straight line which is referred to as the 'cost slope'. The formula for the cost slope is:

$$\frac{\text{Crash Cost} - \text{Normal Cost}}{\text{Normal Time} - \text{Crash Time}}$$

and is defined as the cost of reducing the activity by 1 week. In Figure 6.5 the cost slope is

$$\frac{600 - 300}{5 - 2} = £100/\text{week}.$$

Consider the example of a network shown in Sequenced Gantt Chart form in Figure 6.6 which has associated costs shown in Table 6.1.

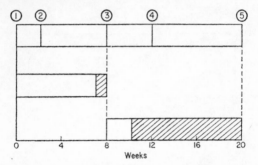

Figure 6.6

Activity Code	Normal Time Wks	Crash Time Wks	Normal Cost £	Crash Cost £	Cost Slope £/Wk
1-2	2	1	150	170	20
1-3	7	5	120	200	40
2-3	6	4	240	300	30
3-4	4	3	40	60	20
3-5	2	1	400	420	20
4-5	8	6	150	250	50

Table 6.1

Consider it is necessary to shrink the project time by 1 week. Three activities have the lowest cost slope, but, because activity 3-5 has float it is ineffective to shrink this activity. Hence this leaves activity 1-2 and activity 3-4. Shrinking activity 1-2 will have the effect of making activity 1-3 critical as well as activities 1-2,

2-3, 3-4, and 4-5. The best course of action would be to shrink activity 3-4. The Sequenced Gantt Chart version of shrinking 3-4 by 1 week is shown in Figure 6.7.

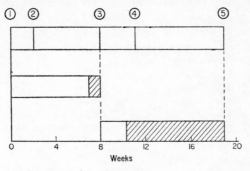

Figure 6.7

If it is desirable to shrink the project by 2 weeks then activities 1-2, and 3-4 would both be reduced by 1 week each. These activities cannot be reduced any further as they are both at crash times. The Sequenced Gantt Chart version of shrinking by 2 weeks is shown in Figure 6.8.

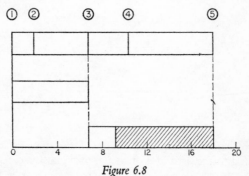

Figure 6.8

It is interesting to see the effect of yet a further reduction. If it is desired to reduce the project by a

65

further week the table of cost slopes would suggest that activity 2–3 should be shrunk at a cost of £30. However, because activity 1–3 is now also critical, the two cost slopes must be added to give a shrinking cost of £30 + £40 = £70. In this case it would be cheaper to shrink activity 4–5 by 1 week at a cost of £50.

The effect of shrinking by 1 week, 2 weeks, and 3 weeks is shown in Table 6.2.

Normal Time	£1,100	20 Weeks
Normal Time—1 Week	£1,120	19 Weeks
Normal Time—2 Weeks	£1,140	18 Weeks
Normal Time—3 Weeks	£1,190	17 Weeks

Table 6.2

Presented with similar information to Table 2 it can be decided where to strike the balance between cost and project duration. The simple example was quite easily manipulated but if it is desired to use C.P.M. on a large scale a suitable computer program should be used. A project cost/time curve that generally results is shown in Figure 6.9.

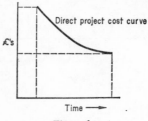

Figure 6.9

No mention has been made of the type of costs related to the activities or to the problems of collating the costs. This is a problem which at times can be very acute. C.P.M. can be an expensive exercise as all the additional cost elements are determined. Usually only the direct costs (e.g. labour, materials, plant hire, etc.) are estimated and the curve in Figure 6.9 is referred to as a 'Direct Project Cost Curve'. The effect of other costs is subjected to a different analysis and these costs, which are indirect costs, are also plotted with respect to time. The recovery of overheads, for instance, will increase with reduction of project duration. Total cost for a project will be the sum of the direct and indirect costs as shown in Figure 6.10. This will give the

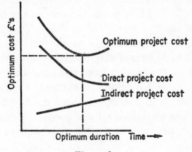

Figure 6.10

'Optimum Project Cost'. It will be noticed that the curve is 'flat' at the minimum, giving a duration range of completion dates for the same cost. Careful interpretation should be made from any C.P.M. cost minimising program because of the difficulty of obtaining cost estimates. Often activities are grouped to facilitate cost analysis and these grouped activities are referred to as 'hammocks' or 'work packages'.

P.E.R.T./Cost

One of the fundamental differences between C.P.A. and P.E.R.T. has already been shown in Chapter 3 with reference to three time estimates for a single activity. Another characteristic of the P.E.R.T. system is to treat money as a resource and manipulate the float to attain the ultimate end of the project with minimum rate of expenditure. When dealing with money as a resource P.E.R.T. is usually referred to as P.E.R.T./Cost.

As with C.P.M. there are difficulties in determining the cost for each activity, and activities are again grouped in 'hammocks' or 'work packages' to facilitate measurement by cost.

However problems still exist, as expenditure is often out of phase with an activity. For example, one consumes domestic electricity (an activity) and then pays for it later. In P.E.R.T./Cost allowances are made for this type of lag.

Refer back for a moment to the payment of the electricity bill. Assume that one has no spare money and has to borrow the money from the bank manager and pay interest as well as capital repayment. The larger the period of the loan the larger the amount of interest payable, hence to reduce interest payments one would seek to delay payment of the bill as long as possible. If one can do this one can claim to have a better 'cash flow position' than one would otherwise have had.

Figure 6.11

On large projects, where expenditure is large it is good business to minimise the rate at which money is spent. P.E.R.T./Cost is also used to control large projects by time and cost as is referred to in Chapter 8.

Figure 6.11 shows the characteristic S-shaped curve

for any large network. Line A shows the cumulative cost of each activity, starting as early as possible, with respect to time. Line B shows the cumulative cost of each activity, starting as late as possible, with respect to time. The latter line shows a better cash flow position. Within limits, the effect of late starting should be investigated with a view to achieving a better cash flow position.

Computer programs are available for costing networks, and P.E.R.T./Cost is more extensively used than C.P.M. P.E.R.T./Cost is used approximately by 5% of all network users, and the emphasis on costing by networks is increasing.

Completion of the Scheduling Phase

The use of float to produce a modified timetable compatible with resources, men, materials, machines, and money, is a complex task. The amount of computation to be carried out is extensive, and it is left to the reader to decide where he wishes to put the chameleon. It must be emphasised that float is there for both resource allocation and to act as a safety valve; hence, never remove all the float. Also, any schedule produced must be implementable and controllable.

[1] *An Introduction to Work Study*, published by The International Labour Organisation.

[2] *Value Analysis* by W. L. Gage, published by McGraw-Hill.

Exercises

1. The network shown below has the following interchangeable resources:

Activity	Resources (Men)
1–5	2
1–15	4
1–20	3
5–15	3
15–20	5

(a) Draw a resource aggregation histogram for activities starting as early as possible.
(b) Allocate resources so that a resource level of 6 is never exceeded.

2. *'Marketing a new product'*. The Sales Director has decided to try and achieve a quicker launch date and has

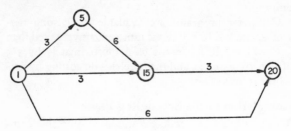

Figure 6.12

received the following suggestions:

(a) 'Deliver Stock to Warehouse' can be speeded up by two weeks using additional contractors at double cost.
(b) 'Package Product', which represents 50% of the project cost, can be speeded up, and the cost will rise from £40,000 to £44,000 for this activity.
(c) 'Transport Stock to Distributors' can be speeded up by two weeks using additional contractors at double cost.

Comment on the implication of starting 'Negotiate Price' and 'Arrange Sales Promotion' as early as possible.

3. *'The television set'*. The Electrical Division of the Manufacturing Company puts in a quote to enable the components to be manufactured at equal cost, and can be dispatched 3 weeks after order.

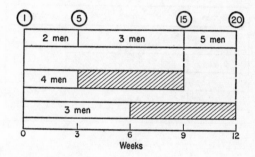

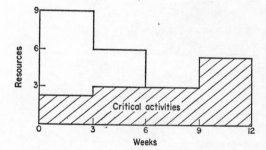

Figure 6.13

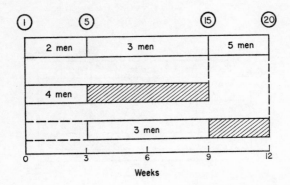

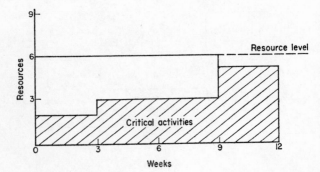

Figure 6.14

The Engineering Maintenance departments can only supply one gang because of holidays, to do the 'modification' and suggest the employment of sub-contractors.

Evaluate these two propositions.

Answers to Exercises

1. (a) See Figure 6.13; (b) See Figure 6.14. Answers to questions 2. and 3. can be formulated using either the analysed network, the tabular analysis, or the Sequenced Gantt Chart. It will be noted how effective the Sequential Gantt Chart is for answering the questions.

2. Suggestion (a) does not affect the critical path. In fact it has 7 weeks float—almost enough to consider using British Road Services!

Suggestion (b) again does not affect the critical path. In fact this is a heavy expenditure item and it should be delayed as much as is safely possible to achieve a better cash flow position.

Suggestion (c) does affect the critical path and it is the only viable suggestion.

'Negotiate Price' has 5 weeks float and this activity could be expanded to facilitate keener and more protracted bargaining if necessary.

If 'Arrange Sales Promotion' starts as early as possible it will finish 11 weeks before the launch date. Hence, this activity should be late started, enabling the Sales Manager to concentrate on the other activities, 'Select Distributors', 'Engage Salesmen', and 'Train Salesmen', or it should be drawn out to allow the advertising to have its desired effect.

3. The effect of the company employing its own resources will reduce the project time and the new critical path will be 1–4–10–15–20–30.

A second engineering gang is not necessary if 'Modify Test Equipment' is started as late as possible.

Note the network manipulations have consumed much of the float resulting in a tighter schedule.

7 THE COMPLETE ARROW DIAGRAM

Aesthetic Appeal

The simplest refinement to a network is to separate out events and duplicate them, triplicate them, etc. as necessary to facilitate better display of networks and

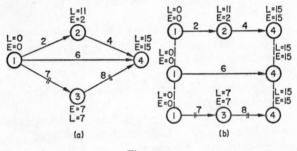

Figure 7.1

improve their aesthetic appeal. Events can be separated out by employing dotted lines. Figure 7.1 shows two identical networks.

The single start event and single finish event rule has not been violated in Figure 7.1 (b) because all three event number 1's are at the same instance in time, and similarly all three event number 4's are at the same instance in time. Analysis of the network is not affected.

Grammatical Dummies

Suppose in the 'Marketing a new product' project the additional activity 'Negotiate Vehicle Hire' were to be included into the network, and was concurrent with 'Select Distributors'. It would appear in the network as shown in Figure 7.2.

Logically Figure 7.2 is correct. However, when the network is analysed by computer tabular analysis each

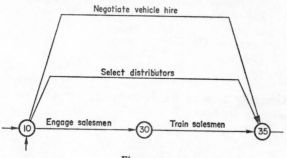

Figure 7.2

activity is recognised by its head and tail event number. In this case both activities 'Negotiate Vehicle Hire' and 'Select Distributors' have the same head and tail event

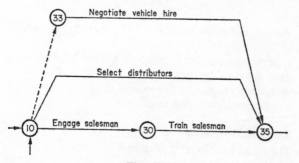

Figure 7.3

numbers. This is an upsetting situation for most computers.

To overcome this a grammatical dummy is employed

75

as in Figure 7.3. A dummy is defined as an activity which has zero time, but otherwise is treated as an activity. Inclusion of the dummy is to facilitate unique numbering codes. Part of the input to the computer would now read

Activity	Code	Duration
Engage Salesmen	10–30	4
Dummy	10–33	0
Negotiate Vehicle hire	10–35	10
Train Salesmen	30–35	2

Table 7.1

Generally speaking the dummy may come before or after the activity:

Figure 7.3 (a) is preferable to Figure 7.3 (b), because

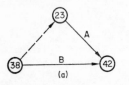
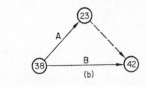

Figure 7.3

certain computer programs have dummy suppression in their output.

If manual analysis is being performed it is not necessary to consider grammatical dummies. Also, some computer programs are specially designed so as not to need grammatical dummies.

Logical Dummies

Dummies have invariably to be incorporated into a network to act as 'one way valves' so that the network means what is intended by the plan.

Consider part of a network, Figure 7.4.

In Figure 7.4 activities D and E cannot start until activities A, B, and C are completed. The planner may wish to state that activity E can start after A, B, and C are completed, and D can start after the completion of A and B.

To maintain this logic a logical dummy, activity

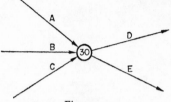

Figure 7.4

25–30, is incorporated as shown in Figure 7.5. In drawing networks it is advisable to recheck the logic when several activities terminate at an event, and several

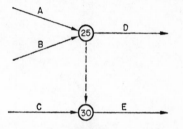

Figure 7.5

activities start at this same event. Figure 7.6 shows the 'Marketing a new product' project extended to include the additional activities.

Negotiate Vehicle Hire	The sales manager will contract hire cars for the salesmen to use after training.
Select Advertising Agency	The sales director will select the agency best suited for the promotion. Thereafter the Advertising Agency will be responsible to the Sales Manager.

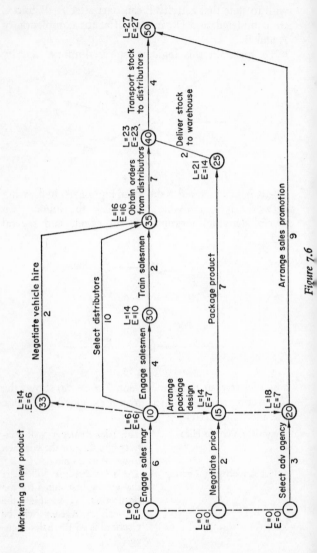

Marketing a new product

Figure 7.6

Activity 10–33 is a grammatical dummy, and activity 15–20 is a logical dummy. Though dummies have no duration, their direction is important and they also appear in the tabular analysis, Table 7.2. Some computer

Activity	Code	Duration	Start E	Start L	Finish E	Finish L	Float T	Float F
Engage Sales Mgr	1–10	6	0	0	6	6	0	0
Negotiate Price	1–15	2	0	12	2	14	12	5
Select Adv Agcy	1–20	3	0	15	3	18	15	4
Approve Pkg Design	10–15	1	6	13	7	14	7	0
Engage Salesmen	10–30	4	6	10	10	14	4	0
Dummy	10–33	0	6	14	6	14	8	0
Select Distribs	10–35	10	6	6	16	16	0	0
Dummy	15–20	0	7	18	7	18	11	0
Package Product	15–25	7	7	14	14	21	7	0
Arr. Sales Promotion	15–50	9	7	18	16	27	11	11
Del. Stock to W'house	25–40	2	14	21	16	23	7	7
Train Salesmen	30–35	2	10	14	12	16	4	4
Neg. Veh. Hire	33–35	2	6	14	8	16	8	8
Obtain Order from Distributors	35–40	7	16	16	23	23	0	0
Transport Stock to Distributors	40–50	4	23	23	27	27	0	0

Table 7.2

programs have a facility which suppresses dummies in printouts. It will be noticed that dummies have float, but this is just the float of the activities which are in the same chain.

Dummies do not appear in bar charts.

Sequential Batching and Ladders

It is often required to split up activities into batches to

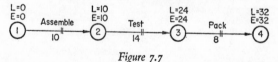

Figure 7.7

enable quicker and more economic manufacture. Consider the network in Figure 7.7. The project as shown by the network would take 32 weeks.

However, if the activities were split up into two batches the network would be:

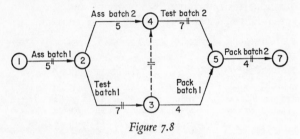

Figure 7.8

Analysis of Figure 7.7 would show a duration of 32 weeks, and Figure 7.8 would show a duration of 23 weeks. Batching and progressively feeding on activities will certainly expedite the project. If, however, the project were to be split up into 3 batches, 4 dummies

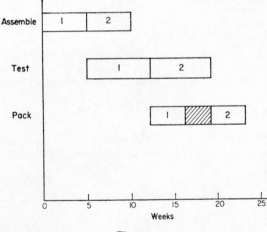

Figure 7.9

would be required. 5 batches would require 10 dummies. It can be seen that by splitting batches the number of dummies increases to an unrealistic situation in which networks cease to be practical.

The bar chart version is shown in Figure 7.9.

The bar chart shows the enforced wait due to the sequential scheduling. This is very common in batch scheduling and care should be taken to spot it. An alternative to Figure 7.8 is to draw the network as a 'ladder' with 'restraint lines' to show the dependencies. Figure 7.10 shows the network in ladder form.

Activities 1–15, and 15–25 are the lead times, and activities 10–20 and 19–23 are the lag times. The lead

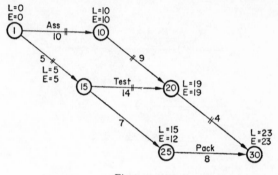

Figure 7.10

time, in the case of activity 1–15, is the time elapsed before activity 15–20 can commence. The lag time, in the case of activity 10–20, is the time elapsed between completion of activity 15–20.

Ladders are a convenient method of displaying progressive feed situations, but caution should be used, as often they are only approximations. In Figure 7.9 it will be noted that packing is not on the critical path!

C.P.A. should not be used for detailed batch scheduling. The complexities and permutations which exist in scheduling is beyond the capability of network. Only the overall batch schedule should be applied to a network. In batch situations the only fool-proof method is to use a bar chart and work out the optimum schedule from it.

Interfacing

The size of networks is often a problem when it comes to controlling projects, and interfacing facilitates the splitting up of networks into sub-networks. For analysis and updating, information from the sub-networks is necessary and the interface events are the links between the networks.

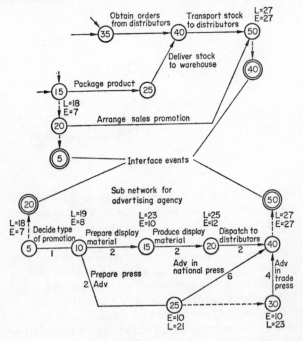

Figure 7.11

Consider that in the 'Marketing a new product' project it is necessary to draw up a separate schedule for the Advertising Agency to cover the activity 'Arrange Sales Promotion'.

The activities involved are
Decide Type of Promotion   1 week
Prepare Displays   2 weeks
Produce Displays   2 weeks
Dispatch Displays to Distributors 2 weeks
Prepare Press Advertising   2 weeks
Advertise in Local Press   6 weeks
Advertise in Trade Press   4 weeks

The networks could be redrawn to include these activities, or interface events could be used as shown in Figure 7.11.

The analysis of the sub-network proceeds as if it were part of the complete network. The earliest time for event 5 is 7 and the forward pass is then completed. The earliest time for event 40 is taken as 27 as the master network controls this time. The backward pass is carried out in the standardised manner.

Zoning

Networks are often drawn to indicate areas of responsibility by separating the events using dotted lines. Figure 7.12 shows the 'Marketing a new product' project displayed with respect to the Buying Department, Sales Department, Production Department, and Shipping Department. Separate tabular analysis and bar chart can also be formulated for each department. A different numbering system is used.

Different Numbering Systems

It is not absolutely necessary to number in ascending

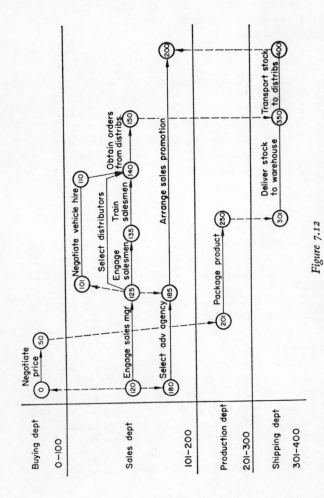

Figure 7.12

84

order, in fact random numbering may be used. Random numbering is often used in very large projects. When networks are drawn to zones each zone is often allocated a group of numbers. E.g.

Buying Department	Nos. 0–100
Sales Department	Nos. 101–200
Production Department	Nos. 201–300
Shipping Department	Nos. 301–400

In this case the numbering system is to go from left to right in ascending order and repeat the process until the whole network is numbered. The ascending system, used throughout this text, is the easiest to use and cross reference between the activity in the tabular analysis and the network is easy.

Different Notations and Conventions

There are no universal standards. The most common conventions have been used in this text. However,

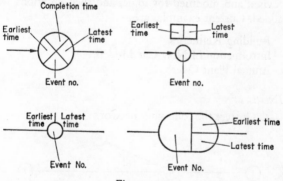

Figure 7.13

events and their associated event times are often expressed in the following different ways.

Ladders are often highlighted by:

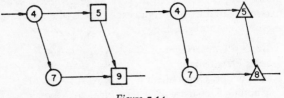

Figure 7.14

Tail events can be referred to as 'i-events', or 'predecessor events'.

Head events can be referred to as 'j-events', or 'successor events'.

Events can be sometimes referred to as nodes.

Package Networks

Projects have a habit of recurring and in certain cases it is worthwhile having standard networks available which often just express the logic. These networks are then revised and modified for logic, and then durations are added. Current examples are:

Building Refineries
Introduction of New Car Models
Annual Plant Overhauls

Exercises

1. Correct the following network:

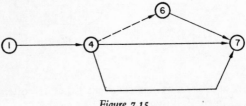

Figure 7.15

2. Correct the following network:

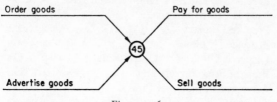

Figure 7.16

3. Draw part of a network diagram showing that activity D depends on the completion of activities A, B, and C; and activity E depends only on the completion of C.

4. Analyse the following network:

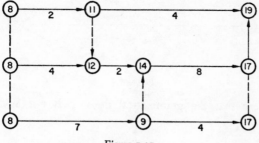

Figure 7.17

5. Draw the network to show a product being *assembled*, *tested* and *packed* in

(a) 3 batches
(b) 5 batches

6. Draw a network to show how the following additional activities comprising 'Arrange Sales Promotion' can be interfaced into the master network for 'Marketing a new product'.

Decide Type of Promotion	1 week
Prepare Salesmen's Demonstration Kits	2 weeks
Issue Kit to Sales Force	2 weeks
Prepare Displays	2 weeks
Produce Displays	2 weeks
Dispatch Displays to Distributors	2 weeks
Prepare Press Advertising	2 weeks
Advertise in National Press	6 weeks
Advertise in Trade Press	4 weeks

7. Analyse the network in Question 6. Can one person prepare the demonstration kits, displays and press advertising?

Answers to Exercises

1.

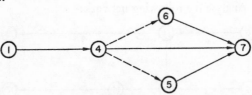

Figure 7.18

(Note that the grammatical dummy is not always required.)

2.

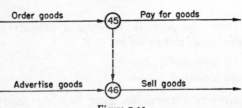

Figure 7.19

(Note that payment of goods only depends on ordering of goods.)

3.

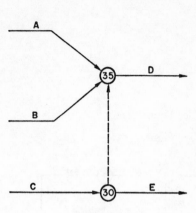

Figure 7.20

(Note that the direction of the dummy is important.)

4.

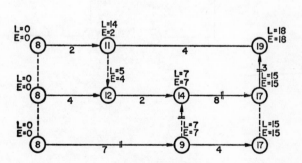

Figure 7.21

5. (a) See Figure 7.22.

(b) See Figure 7.23.

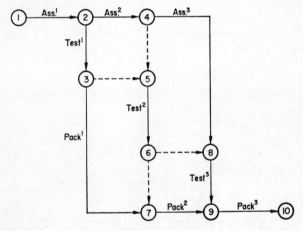

Figure 7.22

The Complete Arrow Diagram

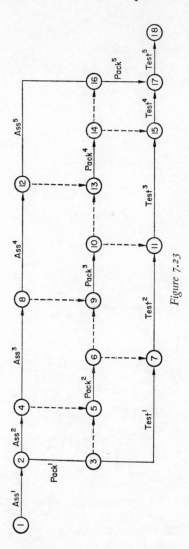

Figure 7.23

6. See Figure 7.24.
7. See Figure 7.25.

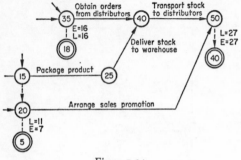

Figure 7.24

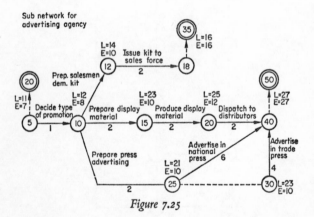

Figure 7.25

7. (Cont.) One person can prepare the demonstration kits, displays, and press advertising if 'Prepare Display Material' and 'Prepare Press Advertising' are late started.

8 CONTROLLING PROJECTS

Project Control

The final phase, and perhaps the most neglected, is the adequate control or monitoring of the project. The control aspect of management is developing into a science in its own right and is frequently referred to as 'Cybernetics'. Control in the mechanical sense is well known, and the steam engine or an old 78 r.p.m. gramophone have built into them a mechanism called a governor which is used to maintain the predetermined speed. The speed may seem constant, but in fact it increases or decreases slightly, and the increase/decrease is detected by the governor which acts in such a way as to bring the speed to the predetermined speed. Without such a device the steam engine or gramophone would race ahead and become inoperative.

In nature as in 'things mechanical' there are governors. Government, the art and science of controlling people, and governor, stem from the same derivation. Society benefits, allegedly, from the government which controls it. The different political forces represent different forms of control.

A project should be similarly governed, that is, it should have a mechanism built into it to facilitate control. In the mechanical sense the control mechanism acts *continuously* and is *automatic* in action. The best example of project control is to consider sailing a ship from London to New York. The course is set and the navigator (project controller) *periodically* takes measurements to compare where the ship is, with where it should be, and *manual adjustments* (turn steering wheel, etc.) are made. The fewer the number of measurements taken by the navigator the greater the risk of being off course, and the greater number of measurements taken the more navigators required. Hence a practical balance is struck for frequency of measurement.

Project control is the taking of measurements during a project, comparing them with the schedule, and making subsequent adjustments. Project control has not yet reached the stage where it is continuous and automatic. For any project, or levels within a project, having established the necessity for control, the review frequency (hourly, daily, weekly, monthly, etc.) should be known; and also, what action should be taken as a result of being ahead or behind schedule.

A schedule is only the best forecast of the future, hence it is expected that activities will not be precisely as per schedule, and the schedule should have a measure of flexibility built into it. Float is the flexibility and the critical activities should be more tightly controlled than the non-critical activities.

Control by Bar Chart

Figure 8.1 shows the bar chart schedule from Chapter 5, Figure 5.1 indicating by a cursor line through week 3,

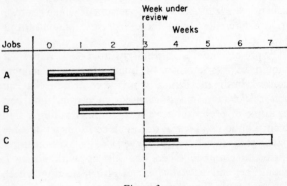

Figure 8.1

that activity A is 100% complete, activity B is 75% complete, and activity C is 25% complete. A glance at the cursor line shows immediately what the situation is.

Bar charting is a quick and visual display of the state of a project. A glance shows that activity A is up to schedule, activity B is 25% behind, and activity C is 25% ahead.

The chart facilitates control as it displays original forecast measurements, actual measurements, and indicates the difference to enable the required action to be taken.

Control by Network

The network could be drawn to scale and the project controlled from it, but since networks are not easy to

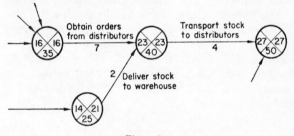

Figure 8.2

draw to scale an alternative method of progressing, from the network, is to use the 'pie chart' notation as shown in Figure 8.2.

When the activities are completed the week number is entered in the north quadrant. Assume the project up to events 15, 20, and 35 has adhered to the schedule, but activity 'Package Product' has taken 9 weeks. The network showing this situation is shown in Figure 8.3.

Progressing in this fashion permits 'Management by Exception'. Since the completion date is within the event slack this delay in 2 weeks will not affect the final completion date. The project control could be delegated to such an extent that management only wishes to know when the completion date exceeds the latest time. Consider further progressing, and assume that activity

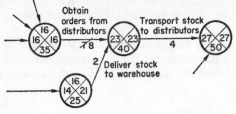

Figure 8.3

'Deliver Stock to Warehouse' has taken 4 weeks and that activity 'Obtain Orders from Distributors' has taken 8 weeks. The network has the disadvantage that it has no facility for recording the fact that activity 'Deliver Stock' has finished in week 20. The network, controlled in this fashion, can only be controlled at the present event times, and partially complete activities cannot be recorded. Figure 8.4 shows the situation of the project at week 24.

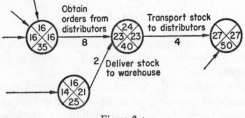

Figure 8.4

At event 40 the latest completion date has been exceeded by 1 week, and unless activity 'Transport Stock to Distributors' can be reduced by 1 week the project will be delayed by this amount.

A useful way of controlling networks is to issue the instructions to start an activity by the use of arrow and event notation. A two-part document, Figure 8.5, is sent to the relevant department. The start date is entered in the original and copy, and the copy is returned to the project controller to signal the start of the activity; and, after the activity is completed, the original is returned, with completion date to the project controller.

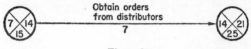

Figure 8.5

Bar charts give a more sensitive control than the network itself because, with bar charts, the progressive state of each activity can be recorded. In networks only the completion of the controlling activity is recorded.

Control by Tabular Analysis

Tabular analysis is the most common form of control when progressing by computer. The tabular analysis already contains the original forecast measurements, and to facilitate control the completion dates of activities, or different durations, is all that is required.

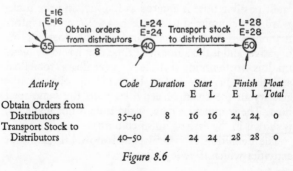

Activity	Code	Duration	Start E	Start L	Finish E	Finish L	Float Total
Obtain Orders from Distributors	35–40	8	16	16	24	24	0
Transport Stock to Distributors	40–50	4	24	24	28	28	0

Figure 8.6

To illustrate control by tabular analysis refer to Figure 8.6, and consider the case where activity 'Obtain Order from Distributors' has taken 8 weeks.

The tabular analysis of the new situation shows that the completion date has been extended by I week.

The format of Figure 8.6 shows the consequences of delay. However, what is often needed is a statement of how to adhere to the completion date already set. The tabular analysis can be represented to show this effect, Figure 8.7.

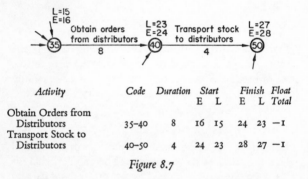

Activity	Code	Duration	Start E	Start L	Finish E	Finish L	Float Total
Obtain Orders from Distributors	35–40	8	16	15	24	23	−1
Transport Stock to Distributors	40–50	4	24	23	28	27	−1

Figure 8.7

In Figure 8.7 the forward pass is completed in the standardised manner giving $E = 28$. However, the latest possible time is entered as $L = 27$, and the backward pass completed to give $E = 15$. When this information is recorded in tabular form the float appears negative, and is the amount of time that has to be made up. It is worth noting that the negative float is total float and this deficiency has to be made up only in one activity in the chain of activities with the same total float. The completion date, if the time is not made up, is shown in the earliest finish column.

The definition of critical path is now "the series of activities which have least float".

C.P.M. and P.E.R.T./Cost Control

The availability of crash times and crash costs in C.P.M. is a useful piece of additional information when deciding what action to take while controlling a project.

P.E.R.T./Cost is useful on very large projects for its additional facility which facilitates cost control by networks, as opposed to time controls mentioned up to

Figure 8.8

now. The cumulative actual costs are compared with planned (budgeted) costs.

In P.E.R.T./Cost estimates are often used for completed activities if the actual costs are not immediately available, and the costs amended when the costs become available to give a more sensitive form of control. The project could be up to date, but over budget; and, it is important to monitor this. Use of P.E.R.T./Cost also allows future trends to be seen in a graphical form. Figure 8.8 shows a P.E.R.T./Cost control graph in which the project at the review date is under budget, but extrapolated trends show that the project will be over budget and beyond target date unless some action is taken.

P.E.R.T./Cost is not a substitute for conventional budgetary control. It is an additional cost control facility which has a faster response than most conventional budgetary control systems.

High Level Control

At high levels of management the need for frequent review is not as great as at lower levels; and certain key events, representative of major accomplishments only, are selected for reporting to top management. These key events are frequently referred to as 'milestones'.

Milestone reporting can be on either a cost or time basis as illustrated in Figures 8.9 and 8.10. The project is back on schedule, but is over budget.

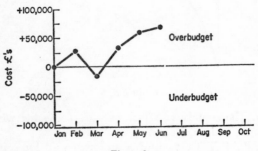

Figure 8.9

Summary for Control

In preparing a schedule 4 questions must always be asked:

1. How often should the project be reviewed?
2. How sensitive should the control be?

3. How should start dates and finish dates be communicated between the project controller and the departments engaged in the activities?

4. What format should be used to monitor progress? Schedules should only be adjusted as necessary. However, C.P.A. is far from a static technique and the whole

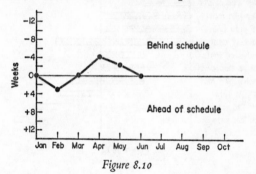

Figure 8.10

network may need replanning as a result of feed back information. One of the assets of C.P.A. is its dynamic nature.

Exercises

1. Draw the bar chart for the 'Television Set' and show the situation at the end of week 8 when the following activities have been completed:

Order Cabinets
Order Electrical Components
Order Packing Material
Modify Production Line
Receive Electrical Components
Receive Packing Material

Modify Test Equipment has started at the earliest possible time and is 25% complete, and the cabinets have been promised in 2 weeks' time.

Does the project controller need to take any action?

Answers to Exercises

1.

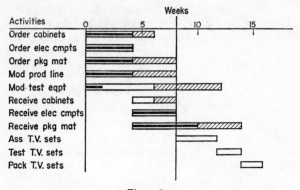

Figure 8.11

Yes, the cabinets have not arrived and assembly cannot take place. A 2 week delivery on the cabinets would only have been acceptable at the latest in week 6. There will be a 2 week delay.

The fact that the test equipment has not been modified is also a problem. It would appear that at 25% completion there would be another $6 - 1\frac{1}{2} = 4\frac{1}{2}$ weeks work to be completed in the remaining 4 weeks float. This can also be shown by showing the bar chart at its latest finishing position:

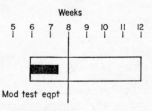

Figure 8.12

However, since this activity was started at its earliest time and only 25% complete, the remaining 75% may well take longer than the 4½ days assumed, and it would be worth further investigation into the cause and effect of this delay.

9 SIMPLIFIED C.P.A.

The 'Bar-Tick' Method

There is often a requirement to use only a small network, and control the project from the network itself or the corresponding bar chart.

A useful method is known as the 'bar tick' method which can be used to analyse the network.

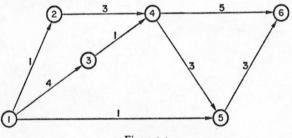

Figure 9.1

The network is drawn in the standardised manner. Consider the network as shown in Figure 9.1.

The Analysis

The method of analysis is a combination of the forward and backward pass to give the critical path in one continuous operation.

The method is to proceed, as in the forward pass, from the start event to determine the earliest events times as shown in Figure 9.2. However, in addition to recording the earliest event times a tick is placed on each activity as shown. In cases where two or more activities converge into the same event a tick is placed *only* on the activity which gives the highest earliest

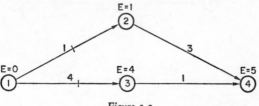

Figure 9.2

event time. The analysis is continued until the final event to give the project duration, see Figure 9.3.

The critical path is determined by starting at the final event and tracing through the path which has a con-

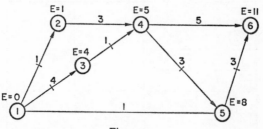

Figure 9.3

tinuous sequence of ticks. Figure 9.4 shows the complete analysis. The critical path is recorded by adding a second tick to the arrow.

The simplified technique only gives the duration and critical path. The amount of float is determined by drawing the Sequenced Gantt Chart version, Figure 9.5, of the network, showing each activity starting at its earliest start date.

A tabular analysis is not necessary, but could be developed from the Sequenced Gantt Chart. Resource

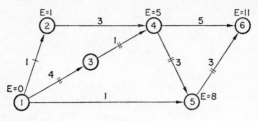

Figure 9.4

allocation, etc. could now follow, as shown in Chapter 6 using this same network.

Inspection will show that activities with total float are shown with a single tick or no ticks. If an activity

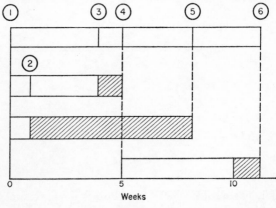

Figure 9.5

has free float it will have no tick at all. The 'bar-tick' method has been so named as 'ticks' find the project duration and critical path, and 'bars' (in this case the Sequenced Gantt Chart) show the float and facilitate further analysis and scheduling.

Exercises

1. Analyse, using the 'bar-tick' method, the 'Marketing a New Product' project network provided, Figure 9.6, to determine the project duration, critical path, and float.

Answers to Exercises

1. See Figures 9.7, 9.8.

Marketing a new product

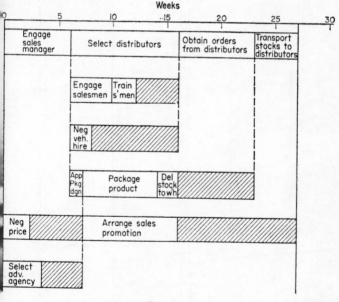

Figure 9.7

Marketing a new product

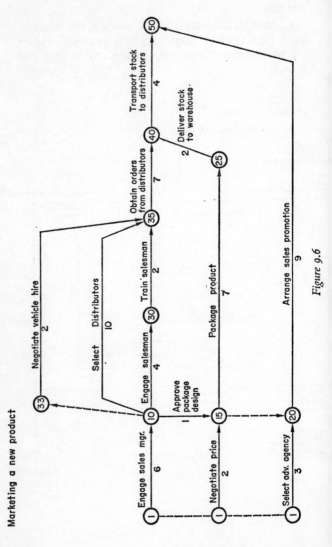

Figure 9.6

Marketing a new product

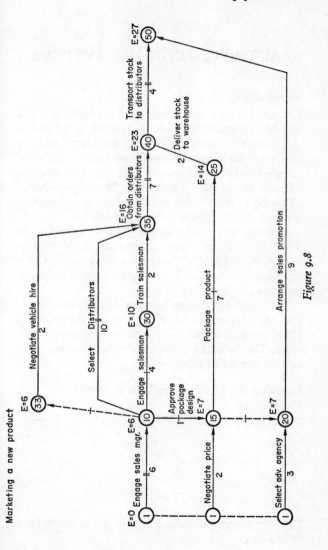

Figure 9.8

10 ACTIVITY-ON-NODE SYSTEMS

Introduction

The text has only so far considered networks in which arrows represent the activities and circles the dependencies, hence the expression 'Activity-on-Arrow' systems. However, there are alternate systems in which the reverse symbolic notation is used. In these systems, referred to in this chapter as 'Activity-on-Node' (A-on-N) systems, circle or nodes represent the activities, and arrows represent the dependencies.

Methods very similar to the general method to be described exist and have names such as 'Method of Potentials', 'M.P.M.', 'Precedence Diagrams', 'Circle and Link Diagrams'. Like any management technique there are also bound to be more.

The essential differences between 'Activity-on-Arrow' and 'Activity-on-Node' systems is in the planning phase, so emphasis will be placed on drawing the network. The usefulness of the term network is that it can be used to refer to either system.

Drawing the Network and the Essential Differences

The network is usually referred to as a 'node' diagram.

Figure 10.1

Consider Figure 10.1, which is part of a network for a Fruit Farm.

In node form, Figure 10.2, the same part of the network would be represented as:

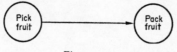

Figure 10.2

As in arrow diagrams the size of the activity circle or length of dependency arrow does not matter.

The advantages claimed for A-on-N are:

1. Easier for the layman to understand.
2. Easier to teach.
3. Quicker to draw.
4. They can handle activity batch splitting and progressive feeding without drawing ladders or dummies.
5. There are no dummies.
6. Easier to modify once drawn.
7. The network need not be drawn; the logic can be developed straight off from the Tabular Display format, and this information fed into a computer. This only generally practicable for small networks.
8. Analysis is similar to 'Activity-on-Arrow' systems.

If the Fruit Farm network is further developed the comparison between the two systems is shown in Figure 10.3 and Figure 10.4.

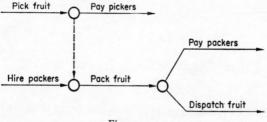

Figure 10.3

Figure 10.4 shows that for node diagrams dummies are unnecessary.

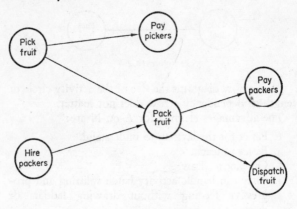

Figure 10.4

Suppose during the preparation of the network it were necessary to add the fact that before the fruit were dispatched it would be necessary to order transport. Figure 10.5 shows that for the arrow diagram a pencil

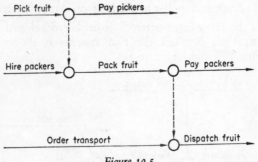

Figure 10.5

and rubber are necessary, plus a dummy to preserve the logic.

ERRATA

Page 27, line 18:	days should read weeks.
Page 28, line 5:	$L = 25$ should read $L = 21$.
Page 87, Figure 7.17:	3 should be inserted between ⑰ and ⑲.
Page 91, Figure 7.23:	Pack[1], Pack[2], etc., should read Test[1], Test[2], etc.; and Test[1], Test[2], etc., should read Pack[1], Pack[2], etc.
Page 113, Figure 10.6:	This should read Figure 10.8.
Page 114, Figure 10.8:	This should read Figure 10.6.
Pages 163, 165 & 166:	All 'T' should be deleted from the computer printouts.

For A-on-N diagrams, Figure 10.6, only one additional dependency and activity is necessary.

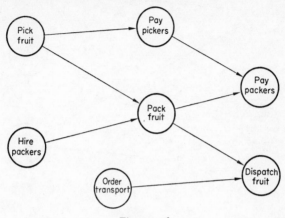

Figure 10.6

Consider it has been decided that the packers are to be paid after paying the pickers. Figure 10.7 shows that the arrow network has to be modified by the use of dummies again.

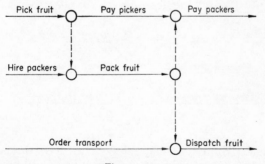

Figure 10.7

For A-on-N diagrams, Figure 10.8, only one additional dependency need be drawn!

5

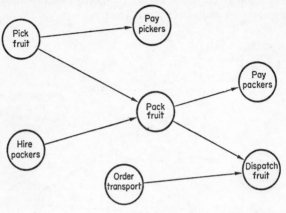

Figure 10.8

However, there is another network comparison which is worth making. Figures 10.9 and 10.10 show the same portion of another network dealing with the 'Last Run of a Product'.

In this case, for aesthetic appeal, the honours fall to the arrow diagram.

An A-on-N network can be formulated into the

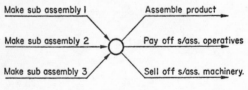

Figure 10.9

tabular format without the need to draw the node diagram. As with the arrow diagram, the tabular format requires the activities to have a unique numbering system, and in this case the activities are numbered, if possible, in ascending order to identify and to facilitate reference. Again, any numbering system can be used.

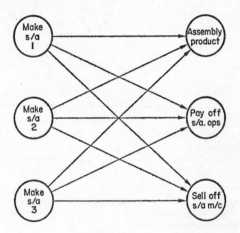

Figure 10.10

Derivation of the tabular display requires a statement of the activities with a reference number. Consider the activities from Figure 10.5. The other approach to drawing the network is to array the activities and reference numbers in a matrix as shown in Table 10.1.

Each square is examined going from L to R horizontally and then down and a tick $(\sqrt{})$ is placed in each square where the vertical activity immediately precedes the horizontal activity. A full house of blanks, going horizontally, are initial activities. A full house of blanks, going vertically, are terminal activities.

From Table 10.1 the A-on-N tabular format is produced as shown by Table 10.2.

	1. Pick Fruit	2. Pay Pickers	3. Hire Packers	4. Pack Fruit	5. Pay Packers	6. Order Transport	7. Dispatch Transport
1. Pick Fruit							
2. Pay Pickers	√						
3. Hire Packers							
4. Pack Fruit			√				
5. Pay Packers				√			
6. Order Transport							
7. Dispatch Transport				√		√	

Table 10.1

Number	Activity	Dependency
1	Pick Fruit	—
2	Pay Pickers	1
3	Hire Packers	—
4	Pack Fruit	3
5	Pay Packers	4
6	Order Transport	—
7	Dispatch Transport	4, 6

Table 10.2

Table 10.1 is an optional extra. Once the activities are listed and numbered Table 10.2 can be developed.

The analysis phase of node diagrams is similar to that of arrow diagrams. Node diagrams are better equipped to handle progressive feeding and batching because they avoid the use of dummies or ladders.

In node diagrams the overlap of one activity upon another is entered on the dependency arrow.

Consider two activities A and B bar charted as shown in Figure 10.11.

It will be seen that overlap + feed = duration of activity A. In A-on-N systems either the feed time or

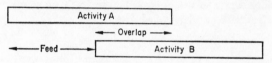

Figure 10.11

the overlap time is entered on to the diagram. This text will consider the method using feed times. However, note that other methods use either overlap or feed.

Various conventions exist for drawing node diagrams. A suitable convention is to square off the circle to permit

Conventions

Dependency	Activity	
	Earliest Start	Latest Start
Feed Time →	Activity Description	
	Duration	Float

better graphical display. Also, dummy activities are *deliberately* introduced to have a single start activity and a single finish activity. These activities have, naturally, zero time.

Analysing the Network

For computer analysis the input is:

Activity, Activity Dependency, Duration, Feed (if any) and Resources (if resource allocation required).

The conventional outputs associated with networks are available. There are fewer computer programs available for A-on-N systems than conventional networks.

Manual computation is by conventional forward and backward pass, and considers earliest and latest starts and float.

Consider a small network, Figure 10.12, analysed by the forward and backward pass.

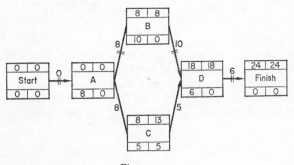

Figure 10.12

For assistance the equivalent bar chart showing earliest starts is shown in Figure 10.13.

On A-on-N the feed time for an activity is entered on the dependency arrow preceding that activity. Since there is no progressive feeding, the feed times are equal to the preceding durations, e.g. the feed time for activity B = 8. The forward pass starts at the start activity for which the earliest start = 0, and the earliest start for A is also = 0. The addition of the feed time of B to the earliest start of A gives the earliest start of B. The forward pass is continued, giving precedence to the highest values of earliest starts until the earliest start of the finish is achieved—this being the project completion time.

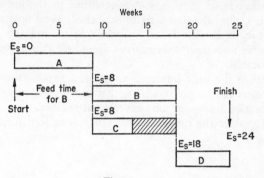

Figure 10.13

The backward pass starts with entering the latest start of the finish equal to the earliest start of the finish. This may sound confusing, but remember that the finish

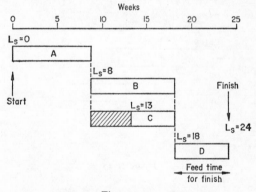

Figure 10.14

is a dummy activity and as such has no duration. Figure 10.14 shows that the latest start for activity D is the latest start of the finish less the feed time for the finish

119

and equals $24 - 6 = 18$. The backward pass is completed by subtracting preceding feed times from succeeding latest starts, giving precedence to the lowest values, until the start activity is reached. Total float, as before, is Earliest Finish — Earliest Start, and this is entered to complete the analysis. Hence the critical path is located.

From the basic information on the diagram tabular formats can be produced, and bar charts and resource allocation follow in the conventional manner.

Consider the network with progressive feed times.

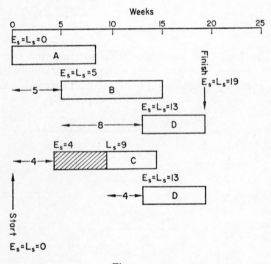

Figure 10.15

Figure 10.15 shows the corresponding bar chart, Figure 10.16 shows the network, and Figure 10.17 shows the 'activity-on-arrow' version using ladders.

The forward and backward pass procedure, Figure

10.16, is carried out in the manner described in the preceding paragraphs. This illustrates the case of analysis when dealing with progressive feed situations.

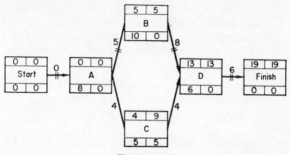

Figure 10.16

To recap on the analysis technique for dealing with ladders the reader is referred back to Chapter 7.

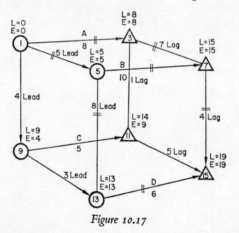

Figure 10.17

Limited Use

The supporters of A-on-N systems find the main advantage lies in the fact that it is easier to draw, and hence the benefits of planning can be achieved with less cost, more quickly, and by more people. The reasons for its limited use with management are:

(1) Arrow diagrams have been universally taught, and hence there is a resistance to change.
(2) A shortage of choice in computer programs, which have not been so fully developed as arrow based networks analysis.

A competent C.P.A. practitioner should be able to switch cheerfully from one system to the other.

Exercises

1. Draw the 'Marketing a new product' project by 'Activity-on-Node'.

2. What is the project duration if stock can be delivered to the warehouse 6 weeks after the start of packing the product, and it is estimated that transport of stock to the distributors can start after half the orders have been obtained from the distributors?

Answers to Exercises

1. See Figure 10.18.

2. See Figure 10.19.

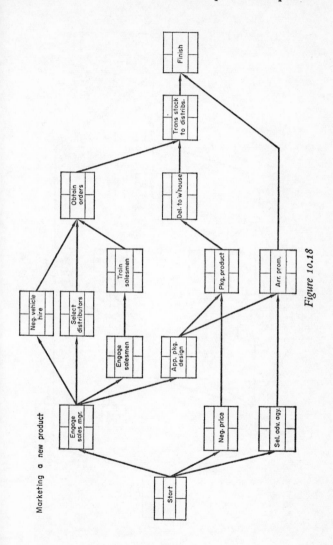

Marketing a new product

Figure 10.18

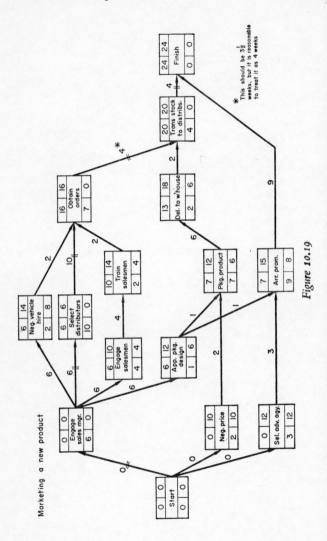

Marketing a new product

Figure 10.19

* This should be 3½ weeks, but it is reasonable to treat it as 4 weeks

11 LINE OF BALANCE

The Use of Line of Balance

Line of Balance (L.O.B.) is a management technique which is allied to Critical Path Analysis. Line of Balance extends the scope of network techniques and is particularly suited to the scheduling and control of projects which are made in fluctuating batches or in repetitive batches.

To apply L.O.B., a study is made of all the activities which make up the final product, and this is translated into an arrow diagram. Also required is the programme showing the quantities to be produced every week or month.

Once the L.O.B. chart is made up, it indicates visually where all phases of production should be at a particular review period, and if the delivery programme will be met. It also shows the current levels of production of each activity against what has been planned. Hence management can take action on the levels which are out of balance. The importance of the technique is that, like C.P.A., it is able to focus the attention of management on those areas which are out of control, thereby allowing the practice of management by exception. If the production of a department is below the L.O.B., action is necessary to maintain the production. If production is above the L.O.B. this may be regarded as safety stock or economic order stock, but it may also be regarded as showing that greater costs have accrued than necessary.

Deriving the Line of Balance

The technique is best explained by reference to a worked example.

A vacuum cleaner is being introduced to the Scandinavian market, and the activities involved are:

Motor Division

Purchase Parts	1 week
Sub-Assembly	3 weeks
Final Assembly	1 week

Casting Division

Purchase Raw Material	1 week
Cast	1 week
Fettle	1 week
Paint	1 week

Manufacture and Assembly Division

Purchase Raw Material	2 weeks
Internal Manufacture	4 weeks
Purchase Sub-Assembly Components	6 weeks
Assemble Sub-Assemblies	1 week
Final Assembly	2 weeks
Purchase Cartons	2 weeks
Pack for Shipment	1 week

The units have to be manufactured to the following schedule:

Week	Planned	Planned Cumulative
1	100	100
2	100	200
3	150	350
4	150	500
5	300	800
6	500	1300
7	400	1700
8	300	2000
9	300	2300
10	200	2500
11	200	2700
12	100	2800
13	100	2900
14	50	2950
15	50	3000

Table 11.1

The conventional method for progressing would be to plot planned cumulative deliveries and actual cumulative deliveries against the corresponding week number as shown in Figure 11.1, the data being compiled in Table 11.2.

Week	Planned	Actual	Planned Cumulative	Actual Cumulative
1	100	100	100	100
2	100	100	200	200
3	150	150	350	350
4	150	150	500	500
5	300	300	800	800
6	500	500	1300	1300
7	400	400	1700	1700
8	300	300	2000	2000
9	300	300	2300	2300
10	200	Nil	2500	2300
11	200	300	2700	2600
12	100		2800	
13	100		2900	
14	50		2950	
15	50		3000	

Table 11.2

The tabular analysis and the graph, Figure 11.1, show that up to week 9 there was no deficiency. However, from week 10 to 11 deficiencies arise. Both the tabular analysis and the graph show the same facts. The advantage of the graph is that it is quicker to interpret and it also shows trends.

The chart, Figure 11.1, states problems rather than solves them as it does not show which division is responsible for the deficiency, nor does it provide an early warning system. Line of Balance is designed to overcome these deficiencies.

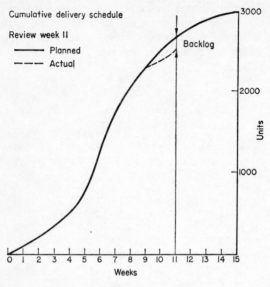

Figure 11.1

The procedure for L.O.B. is:

1. Draw an arrow diagram of the process as in C.P.A., but have as many single event starts as there are separate departments.
2. Number the events. It is advisable to work backwards. The number of the last event will be the number of activities plus one.
3. Enter the activity times.
4. Proceed to determine the number of weeks (B) that each event is behind the finish of the last activity. This is done by taking the last event (No. 15) as B = 0 and, working backwards, adding the duration of each activity cumulatively.

In effect this is saying that any work which has been fettled will be ready for shipment in 4 weeks time.

Figure 11.2 shows steps 1 to 4.

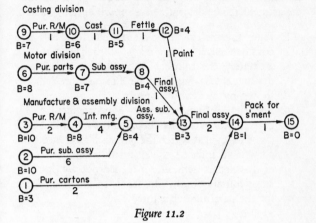

Figure 11.2

5. Draw up a Cumulative Delivery Schedule as in Table 1.
6. Plot Cumulative Delivery against Week Number on the L.O.B. Chart, Figure 11.3, and enter the Departmental Activities.

Assume one is concerned with determining what should be the production level in each department. Since there is a fluctuating delivery schedule and a time lag in manufacture, the number of units of production in each department will vary. L.O.B. enables the number of units in each department to be determined graphically. Consider the construction of a L.O.B. chart for week 7. The schedule demands a cumulative output of 1700 units. The finished units produced in week 7 would have passed through the painting department in week 4, since the arrow diagram shows that it takes a further 3 weeks to complete the cleaner after painting. Conversely, at the end of week 7 any finished units in the

129

painting department should be ready for shipment at the end of week 10. The production level of each department can be determined as shown in steps 8 and 9.

8. Enter the review week on the chart. In this case consider week 7 and add for each department separately the number of weeks by which that department is lagging the finished product, as shown by the arrow diagram.
9. For each department, erect a perpendicular (A), corresponding to that department's relative time lag. The level at which the perpendicular meets the curve will indicate the planned cumulative level of that department, and it is recorded by drawing a horizontal line (B). This has been shown in detail for the painting department.

Hence, after completion of step 9, a 'Line of Balance' has been determined for all departments for week 7. Figure 11.3 shows steps 5 to 9.

10. Enter the actual number of units in each department by drawing bar charts for each department.
11. The number of units over the L.O.B. is the extent of over-production, and anything below the line is under-production. The chart shows that the planned output for week 10 will be units short unless action is taken in the painting department in week 7. Hence the use of L.O.B. as an early warning device.

Figure 11.4 shows steps 10 to 11.

The L.O.B. chart can also be represented functionally. For example consider the Purchasing Department responsibilities as in Figure 11.5.

The results from the L.O.B. chart can be tabulated, as Table 11.3, and this shows that action is only necessary where the system is out of balance.

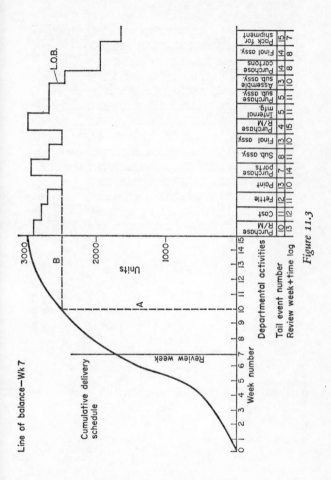

Figure 11.3

Line of balance—Wk 7

Departmental activities	Purchase R/M	Cast	Fettle	Point	Purchase parts	Sub. assy.	Final assy.	Purchase R/M	Internal mfg.	Purchase sub. assy.	Assemble sub. assy.	Purchase cartons	Final assy.	Pack for shipment
Tail event number	10	11	12	13	7	8	13	4	5	5	13	14	14	15
Review week+time lag	13	12	12	10	14	11	10	15	11	11	10	8	8	7

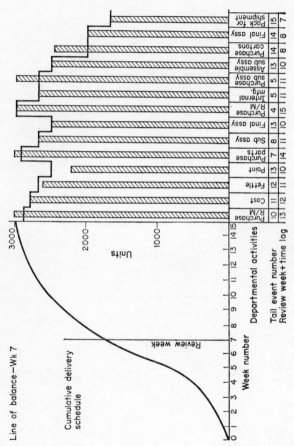

Figure 11.4

Computer programs are available for L.O.B. An interesting program is available called PERT/LOB which interfaces both techniques and allows complete

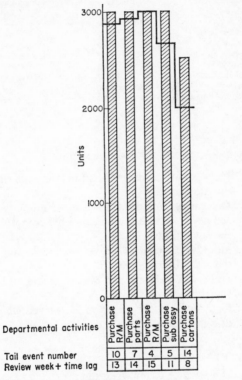

Figure 11.5

computer planning, scheduling and control of product development through transition to completed production.

Line of Balance can be seen to be a very useful graphic technique. Once set up it can be manipulated easily.

Departmental Activity	L.O.B.	Actual	Difference	Action
Purchase R/M	2900	3000	+100	Inform Dept Mgr.
Cast	2800	2800	—	—
Fettle	2700	2600	−100	Inform Dept Mgr.
Paint	2500	2200	−300	Inform Dept Mgr.
Purchase Parts	2950	3000	+50	Inform Dept Mgr.
Sub-Assy	2700	2700	—	—
Final Assy	2500	2500	—	—
Purchase R/M	3000	3000	—	—
Internal Mfg	2700	2700	—	—
Purchase Sub-Assy	2700	3000	+300	Inform Dept Mgr.
Assemble Sub-Assy	2500	2500	—	—
Purchase Cartons	2000	2500	+500	Inform Dept Mgr.
Final Assy	2500	2500	—	—
Pack for Shipment	1700	1700	—	—

Table 11.3

The following is a recap of the steps.

1. Draw an arrow diagram, number events, and add duration times.
2. Determine the number of weeks/months each activity is cumulatively behind the completion of the last activity.
3. Plot the cumulative delivery schedule and enter the activities on the chart.
4. Draw a L.O.B. for the review period and enter actual production levels.
5. Compare and take action on those levels which are out of balance.

Exercises

1. Draw a L.O.B. for week 5 in the chapter example.
2. Draw a L.O.B. for week 10 in the chapter example.
3. Draw a L.O.B. chart and arrow diagram for the manufacture of Frequency Modulators. Consider the review period as week 10.

The Frequency Modulator is made from two parts, sub-assembly 1 and sub-assembly 2.

Sub-Assembly 1 passes through 5 stages:

1. Purchase Raw Material	1 week
2. First Manufacturing Process	3 weeks
3. Second Manufacturing Process	2 weeks
4. Third Manufacturing Process	2 weeks
5. Painting	1 week

Sub-Assembly 2 passes through 5 stages:

1. Purchase Components	2 weeks
2. First Assembly	3 weeks
3. Test First Assembly	2 weeks
4. Calibration	2 weeks
5. Seal Off	2 weeks

Final Assembly

1. Assemble Sub-Assembly 1 to Sub-Assembly 2	2 weeks

Delivery Schedule

Week	Number	Week	Number
1	10	14	30
2	10	15	30
3	12	16	25
4	13	17	25
5	15	18	20
6	20	19	20
7	20	20	15
8	20	21	15
9	25	22	15
10	30	23	13
11	30	24	12
12	30	25	10
13	35		

From the chart read off how many Sub-Assemblies 1 and Sub-Assemblies 2 should have been made.

500 sets of Sub-Assembly Raw Material have been purchased. Is this reasonable? Is there any significance in the fact that 400 sets of components have been received for Sub-Assembly 2?

Critical Path Analysis

Answers to Exercises

1. and 2. See Line of Balance Chart (Figure 11.6).

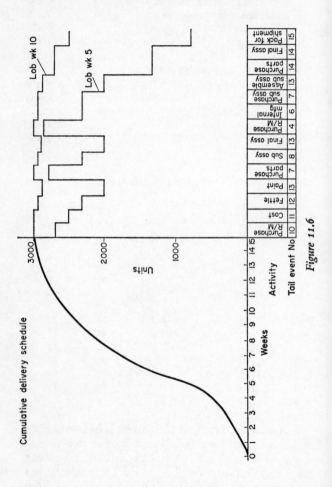

Figure 11.6

Flow chart – frequency modulator

Sub-assembly I.

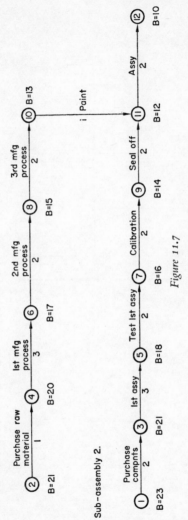

Sub-assembly 2.

Figure 11.7

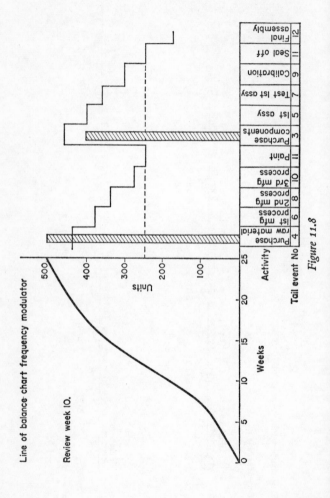

Figure 11.8

3. See Figures 11.7 and 11.8. The finished S/A 1 and S/A 2 parts should be at event 11, and correspond to the quantity 'painted' and 'sealed off'. The fact that there are 500 sets of 'raw material' is insignificant. This represents more than is necessary but the material is likely to be bought in certain batch quantities. S/A 2 is short of 'purchased components' by 50 sets. This means that in week 21 (see the flow chart for event 3) there will be a deficiency of 50 sets unless action is taken to correct the situation. There is $21 - 10 = 11$ weeks to make up this deficiency. This shows the effectiveness of control by Line of Balance.

12 SUMMARY OF CRITICAL PATH ANALYSIS

The Use and Need for C.P.A.

Critical Path Analysis is a powerful planning technique, with subsequent benefits, that is well proven in short (30 activities upwards), medium, and large complex, mainly non-repetitive situations.

The use of Line of Balance extends the power of C.P.A. into many repetitive situations.

The use of network techniques will expand as businesses demand more of a manager's time and skills. Business operations are increasing in complexity, and profit margins are being continually squeezed; and, as a result, more is being asked of management. To maintain high standards of performance more emphasis is being placed on 'management methods' and 'management techniques'. Critical Path Analysis is one of the modern breed of management techniques.

The Distinct Features of C.P.A.

1. *Goals Have to be Set.* Before planning can begin, the objectives of a project, and how they are to be achieved, have to be stated.
2. *Enforces Planning.* To prepare a network the planner must start collating information from all sources liable to be engaged in the project. The resultant information is then logically put together. The planners are forced to dig deeper than previously with subsequent benefits.
3. *Policy Statement.* The relationship between the activities is clearly shown; and the project, symbolically represented, shows the interactions of all participants.

A flow of information exists that binds together the activities and the management involved. A management with previous poor planning may find that for a project steps 1, 2, and 3 may be all that is sufficient to give 80% of the total benefit of C.P.A.

4. *Model Building*. No designer just makes a ship; he makes a 'scalar model' of the hull, and tests the hull. From the results of his tests and analysis with the model he is able to make certain predictions. Similarly the planner is now able to make a 'symbolic model', subject the model (network) to analysis, and make certain forecasts. The idea of making symbolic models is characteristic of Operational Research[1] techniques, one of which is C.P.A.

5. *Model Analysis*. Model analysis yields cost and time information on:

   1. Project Duration
   2. Critical and Sub-Critical Activities
   3. Activity Start and Finish Schedule, and Float Available
   4. Where effectively to apply Cost Reduction Techniques
   5. How to Allocate or Reallocate Resources
   6. The effects of modifying the plan.

6. *Aid to Communication*. The plan can be presented in 3 separate formats:

   1. Arrow Diagram
   2. Tabular Analysis
   3. Bar Chart.

   Areas of responsibility can be indicated, and each area presented with its own network in the required format.

7. *Facilitates Control*. C.P.A. permits the practice of management by exception, in that management need

only act when the situation is out of control. Measurements of actual achievements are recorded against forecast. The difference, if any, becomes the catalyst for management action. The remaining part of the network will give management guidance on what action to take, and the probable results of certain courses of action.

8. *Assists in Tendering for Contracts.* A tender for a contract, planned by C.P.A., has a better chance of being accepted because the potential customer knows that the tender is likely to be more accurately costed than otherwise. Also, having allocated a tender, the customer can follow the progress of the order from the suppliers' network. Many contracts stipulate the use of C.P.A. and/or L.O.B.

The Introduction of C.P.A.

C.P.A. is logic and basic mathematics, which even the innumerate can understand. However, to achieve the pay off from the technique personnel must be trained and experienced in the technique; and also, be prepared to accept the discipline the technique enforces.

Advice on training can be obtained from Companies using C.P.A., Polytechnics, and Management Consultants. Consultants have the added benefit of offering in-plant training.

Two levels of training are essential:

1. Practitioner Training (1–3 weeks) for the technique.
2. Managerial Appreciation (1–3 days) to understand the discipline C.P.A. gives an organisation.

Despite the fact that C.P.A. is quantitative, there are no real figures available for the potential saving from use of the technique. Many qualitative savings have been made, and documented.[1]

[1] 18 *Case Studies in Critical Path Analysis*, British Productivity Council.

Two useful films are available on hire from the Central Film Library.[1] The first deals with the techniques, and the second shows the technique working and the interaction of the people concerned.

C.P.A. will not solve problems nor make decisions. It is an aid to the problem solving process in complex planning. Management must also decide how far they should go—should they use computers, resource allocation programs, P.E.R.T./Cost; or should they start off with simple networks and manually compute? It would be foolish to answer this question, but a guideline would be consult a company which has successfully trodden the critical path—there are many.

[1] "Critical Path," Ref. No. U.K. 1745; "Critical Path Analysis in Use", Ref. No. U.K. 1826.

CRITICAL PATH ANALYSIS

Planning Phase	*Scheduling Phase*	*Controlling Phase*
—Presentation of the Arrow Diagram or Network with regard to precedence and inter-relationships of activities	—Reconciliation of Plan to implementable Schedule with regard to resources	—Communication and Monitoring the use of resources
Activities Description Events Number	Add Estimates of Duration	Four Decisions —How to Communicate Starts and Finishes? —How often to Review? —How sensitive should the Control be? —Which Format to Use?
Single Start Event Single Finish Event	Forward Pass—Project Duration Backward Pass—Critical Path	
Time Flows in Arrow Direction Use Dummies if required	Event Slack—From Earliest and Latest Event Times Tabular Analysis —Earliest, Latest, Starts and Finishes —Float: Total and Free	Types of Format —Network itself —Bar Chart —Sequenced Gantt Chart —Tabular Analysis —Cumulative Cost
Logical Expression only	Bar Chart or Sequenced Gantt Chart	
Interfacing —For Sub-Division —For Connecting Networks	Further Resource Allocation —Manpower —Machines —Money	
Ladders—Use in lieu of dummies for Progressive Feed, use carefully	Result: Schedule Compatible to Resources Available	
Result: Network in Arrow Diagram or Tabular Format		Result: Goals Reached more Painlessly and Effectively

Key Points in Critical Path Analysis

CRITICAL PATH ANALYSIS

Powerful, Accurate, Precise Management Information System for

>*Planning*
>*Scheduling*
>*Controlling*

Small, Medium, Large Projects Characterised by

Their Non-Repetitive Nature

With regard to

>*Time*
>*Manpower*
>*Machines*
>*Materials*
>*Equipment*
>*Money*

Facilities Offered by Computers

Input Required   Activity
Event by Head and Tail Number (i-node and j-node).
Duration.
Start Date or Week Number.
Department.
Completion Dates, or Week Numbers for Controlling the Project.

Optional Extras

Resources, Normal Resources and Threshold Resources; Normal Time, and Threshold Time.
Costs, Normal Costs, and Crash Costs; Normal Time, and Crash Time.

Output Received	Tabular Analysis by Project or Department

    —In order of Ascending Event Codes.
    —In order of Descending Float.
Bar Charts by Project or Department.
Monitoring by Bar Chart and/or Tabular Analysis.

Optional Extras

Resource Aggregation for each Resource at
    —Earliest Start.
    —Latest Start.
Resource Allocation to meet Normal Resources, and minimum Time extension if necessary.
Resource Allocation to meet Time and Resources using Threshold Resources when necessary, or extending into Threshold Time.
PERT/Cost by Table or Graph of cumulative costs.
CPM for guidance in reduction of project time.
Monitoring by all the optional extras.

Practical Application of a Project Check List

An organisation engaging in critical path analysis will find the items below form a useful check list.

Preparation of the Work List

1. How should the work list be built up?

2. How detailed should the activities be?

3. How can it be ensured that each Department's requirements are included?

4. How should contractor's work be dealt with?

5. How should activity durations, and the corresponding manpower and equipment be estimated?

Drawing the Arrow Diagrams

1. Who should draw the arrow diagram?

2. How can the interactions of the different Departments, Contractors and Consultants be phased?

3. How should the arrow diagram be drawn, presented and distributed?

4. What level of detail should be incorporated into the diagram?

5. If the project has logical links with other projects in hand, how should these be co-ordinated and programmed?

6. How should the logic of the arrow diagram be checked?

Analysis of the Network

1. How should the network be analysed? e.g. by hand, or by computer.

Control of the Project

1. How should the men involved in the project be made aware of the plan?

2. How should the activity starts and finishes be issued and recorded?

3. What planning and control aids are needed?

4. Who should be responsible for the overall control?

5. How frequently should planning programmes be reviewed?

6. How much of a variance is necessary before action is taken?

7. Should some form of cost control be run in parallel with the work progress system? How can activities be costed?

CASE STUDY 1

13 INSTALLING A COMPUTER BUREAU

A company is installing a computer and the project has the following activities and durations.

Staff

Appoint Manager	2 weeks
Recruit Staff	4
Arrange Training	2
Train Staff	4

Installation

Order Computer	12
Decide Bureau Layout	1
Provide Services for Computer	3
Test Services for Computer	2
Install Computer	3
Manufacturer Test Computer	1
Company Take Over Computer	2
Prepare Two Initial Programs (after take over)	See below
Operational Run	1

The activity 'Prepare Two Initial Programs' is estimated to consist of:

Systems Engineering	10 weeks
Write Programs	14
Prepare Programs	8
Test Programs	4

The time of one program is half the estimates given, and the activity 'Prepare Program' can be batched. Prepare:

1. Network zoned to show Staff and Installation responsibilities.
2. Analyse network via network itself and by Tabular Analysis.
3. Determine Project Duration and Critical Path.
4. Draw the Sequenced Gantt Chart.
5. Draw the 'activity-on-node' version for the activity 'Prepare Two Initial Programs'.

Answers to Case Study 1

1. and 2. See Networks (Figs. 13.1, 13.2) and Tabular Analysis.

TABULAR ANALYSIS

Activity	Code	Duration	Start		Finish		Float	
			E	L	E	L	T	F
Decide Layout	1–5	2	0	6	2	8	6	0
Appoint Mgr	1–6	2	0	6	2	8	6	0
Order Computer	1–15	12	0	0	12	12	0	0
Provide Services	5–10	2	1	8	3	10	6	0
Dummy	6–12	0	2	10	2	10	8	0
Recruit Staff	6–18	4	2	8	6	12	6	0
Test Services	10–15	2	4	10	6	12	6	6
Arrange Training	12–18	2	2	10	4	12	8	2
Install	15–20	3	12	12	15	15	0	0
Train	18–25	4	6	12	10	16	6	6
Mfg. Test	20–25	1	15	15	16	16	0	0
Take Over	25–30	2	16	16	18	18	0	0
Systems Eng	30–31	10	18	18	28	28	0	0
Lead	30–32	5	18	18	23	23	0	0
Lag	31–33	9	28	28	37	37	0	0
Write Programs	32–33	14	23	23	37	37	0	0
Lead	32–34	7	23	23	30	30	0	0
Lag	33–35	4	37	37	41	41	0	0
Prepare Programs	34–35	8	30	33	38	41	3	3
Lead	34–36	4	30	35	34	39	5	0
Lag	35–37	4	41	41	45	45	0	0
Test Programs	36–37	4	34	39	38	43	5	5
Operational Run	37–40	1	43	43	44	44	0	0

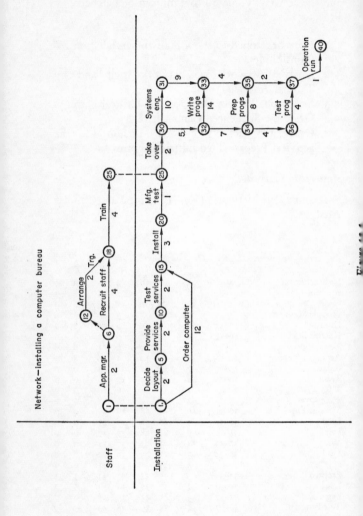

Network—installing a computer bureau

Figure 13.1

Network—installing a computer bureau

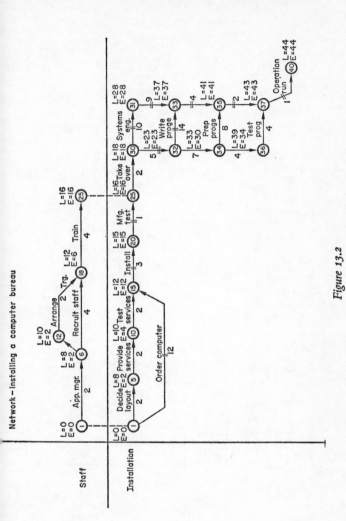

Figure 13.2

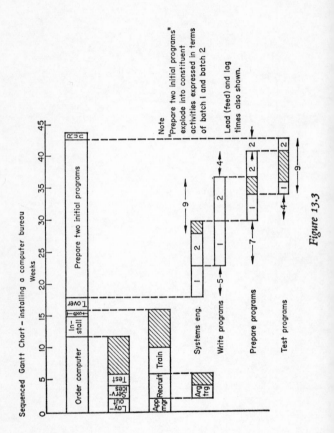

Figure 13.3

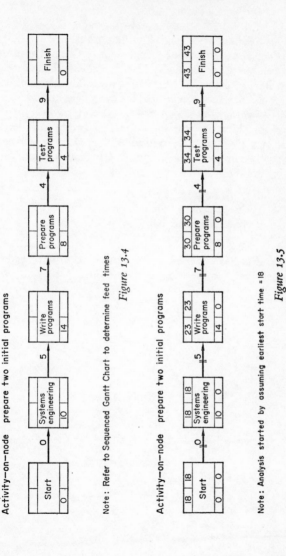

Activity—on—node   prepare two initial programs

Start	Systems engineering	Write programs	Prepare programs	Test programs	Finish
0	0 → 10 →	5 → 14 →	7 → 8 →	4 → 4 →	9 → 0

Note: Refer to Sequenced Gantt Chart to determine feed times

Figure 13.4

Activity—on—node   prepare two initial programs

Start	Systems engineering	Write programs	Prepare programs	Test programs	Finish
18 18	18 18	23 23	30 30	34 34	43 43
Start 0	0 Systems engineering 10	5 Write programs 14	7 Prepare programs 8	4 Test programs 4	9 Finish 0

Note: Analysis started by assuming earliest start time = 18

Figure 13.5

153

3. Project Duration 44 weeks.
   Critical Path 1–15–20–25–30–40.

4. See illustration (Fig. 13.3). The problem of handling ladders is shown by the Sequenced Gantt Chart. The float given by the tabular analysis is meaningless when related to the three activities. The float is a measure of the internal interference due to sequential batching. The critical path is shown as 1–15–20–25–30–31–33, and 30–32–33–35–37–40. This is only the approximate solution, as the lead or lags are apparently critical and 'Prepare Programs' and 'Test Programs' are not critical. In reality the critical activities are:

Systems Engineering Batch 1.
Write Programs Batch 1 and 2.
Prepare Programs Batch 2.
Test Program Batch 2.

5. and 6. See Network and Analysed Network (Figures 13.4, 13.5).

CASE STUDY 2

14 BUILDING A V.H.F. TRANSMITTING STATION

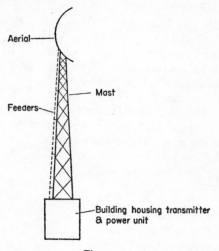

Figure 14.1

It has been decided to build a V.H.F. Transmitting Station and a list of activities, and associated durations, has been drawn up. The design and specifications have been agreed, and the different contracts placed. Building of the transmitter is the responsibility of the Planning and Installation Department (P.I.D.) which has the following sections:

A Transmitter Services Unit
A Power Services Unit

A Construction Department—Bricks
A Construction Department—Masts
An Aerial Services Unit

When the Transmitting Station is completed it will be the responsibility of the Operating and Maintenance Department.

The activities are:

Transmitter Services Unit (TSU)

Manufacture Transmitter (Tx)	63 days
Works Test Tx	1
Deliver Tx to Site	1
Install Tx and connect to L.T.	4
Manufacturer aligns and tests Tx with Dummy Aerial	6
P.I.D. tests completed Transmitter Station	2
Operating and Maintenance Department test and accept Transmitting Station	2
Trade Tests	2
Stereo Tests (concurrent with Trade Tests)	1

Power Services Unit (PSU)

Manufacture Power Unit	28
Deliver Power Unit	1
Electricity Board to supply H.T.	42
Connect Power Unit to H.T. Supply	7

Construction Department—Bricks (CDB)

Deliver Building Materials	21
Build Access Road	4
Build to Roof Level (stage 1)	24
Complete building to Power Unit Access (stage 2)	9
Complete Building to Tx Access (stage 3)	4
Complete Building (stage 4)	8

Construction Department—Masts (CDM)

Manufacture Prefabricated Mast	9
Deliver Prefabricated Mast to Site	1
First Stage in Mast Fabrication	18
Complete Mast	18
Erect Hoist	1

Aerial Services Unit (ASU)

Manufacture Aerial	78
Deliver Aerial	1
Erect Aerial	4
Manufacture Feeders	21
Deliver Feeders	3
Erect Feeders	4
Manufacturer Aligns and Tests Aerial	7
Connect Aerial to Tx	1

Notes

1. The activities have been collected from each section of P.I.D. by the project co-ordinator, and are in order of sequence as far as possible. There are several technicalities which need explanation. The term 'transmitter' has a dual meaning. It refers essentially to electronics that produce the wireless broadcast signals, but it is also a generic term for a 'transmitter station'. In the context of the exercise, 'transmitter or Tx' refers to the electronics only. To power the transmitter it is necessary to convert the electricity High Tension supply (H.T.) to a Low Tension Supply (L.T.) and this function is performed by the power unit.

The access road is only necessary to reinforce the road for delivery of the mast.

The building is constructed in four sequential stages. The mast, erected in two stages, can be erected once the roof is finished. For safety reasons the power access and transmitter access are not completed until the roof is on. The feeders are erected after the mast completion and then connected to the aerial. The Stereo and Trade Tests are concurrent activities.

If the reader has a problem with the technicalities, the best analogy is to consider a domestic T.V. installation. The 'set' is analogous to the 'transmitter', and the 'H' is the 'aerial'. The 'chimney' is the 'mast', and the 'coaxial wire' connecting the set to the aerial is the 'feeder'. The 'domestic electricity supply' is the 'power unit'.

Questions

1. Draw the Network. Show the Critical Path and determine the Project Duration.

2. Compute the Tabular Analysis for

    (1) Ascending event code order
    (2) Ascending float order
    (3) Critical activities only

3. Draw a bar chart to show the activities for the Aerial Services Unit.

4. Suggest a graphical format which would facilitate weekly control.

5. All 5 Departments supply their own skilled labour from central workshops. Unskilled labour is recruited locally by the site manager. Unskilled labour requirements are:

Transmitter Services Unit

Install Tx and connect to L.T.	4 men
Manufacturer aligns and tests Tx with Dummy Aerial	2 men

Power Services Unit

Connect Power Unit to H.T. Supply	4 men

Construction Department—Bricks

Deliver Building Materials	2 men

Build Access Road	4 men
Build to Roof Level (Stage 1)	12 men
Complete Building to Power Unit Access (Stage 2)	4 men
Complete Building to Tx Access (Stage 3)	4 men
Complete Building (Stage 4)	6 men

Construction Department—Masts

First Stage in Mast Fabrication	8 men
Complete Mast	6 men
Erect Hoist	6 men

Aerial Services Unit

Erect Aerial	6 men
Erect Feeders	8 men

Draw a resource aggregation histogram to show the number of unskilled men on the project. (Use earliest start times.)

6. Show the project at the end of week 9. The reported status of the activities is:

TSU

Manufacture Transmitter (1–10)	75% complete

PSU

Electricity Board to Supply H.T. (1–28)	Complete
Manufacture Power Unit (1–15)	Will begin at the start of week 10

CDB

Deliver Building Materials (1–5)	Complete
Build to Roof Level (5–21)	Complete
Build Access Road (5–9)	Complete

CDM

Manufacture Mast (1–9)	Complete
Deliver Mast (9–22) expected at the start of week 10	

ASU

Manufacture Feeders (1–35)	Complete
Deliver Feeders (35–50)	due to arrive in 2 days
Manufacture Aerial (1–12)	75% complete

7. Draw the Network using Activity-on-Node.

8. Analyse the answer to Question 7.

Answers

1. The network is shown analysed: Figure 14.2. The critical path is 1–5–21–22–40–45–50–55–65–70–80–90–100–110. The critical path changes from CDB, to CDM, ASU, to TSU. The duration is 104 days. Note that your answer may 'look' different from the model answer provided. After drawing networks are tidied up for good presentation.

2. See computer printouts 1, 2, and 3. Necessary input was activity, predecessor event, successor event, report code, and duration.

3. See computer printout 4. **A**, represents 1 day project duration, **C**, represents 1 day product duration for critical activities. Note computer printout width restricts printout, hence it is given in two printouts. Float is shown by......

4. Refer to Sequenced Gantt Chart: Figure 14.3. Drawn by sectional responsibilities.

5. Refer to Resource Aggregation Histogram: Figure 14.4.

6. Refer to Sequenced Gantt Chart: Figure 14.5.

All activities are up to date except 'Manufacture Transmitter' and 'Manufacture Aerial', which are ahead; and except 'Manufacture Power Unit' (1–10), 'Deliver Mast' (9–22), 'Deliver Feeders' (35–50), which are behind.

Examining each delayed activity in isolation it can be seen that

(a) for *Manufacture Power Unit* (1–15) there are 35 days float left from week 9 on the chains 28–30–60–70–80. Providing this activity starts in week 10 (day 45)

Building a V.H.F transmitter station
Network

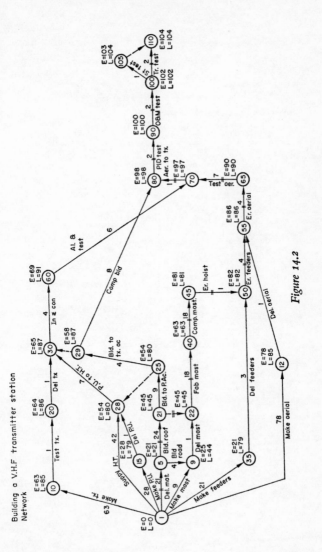

Figure 14.2

Critical Path Analysis

I.C.T. 1900 SERIES PERT   24/06/68

PROJECT TS   BUILDING A TRANSMITTER STATION

ACTIVITIES IN EARLY START ORDER

PREC EVENT	SUCC EVENT	REPORT CODE	DESCRIPTION
1	5	CDB	DELIVER BUILDING MATERIALS
1	9	CDM	MANUFACTURE MAST
1	10	TSU	MANUFACTURE TRANSMITTER
1	12	ASU	MANUFACTURE AERIALS
1	15	PSU	MANUFACTURE POWER UNIT
1	28	PSU	E. BOARD SUPPLY H.T.
1	35	ASU	MANUFACTURE FEEDERS
5	9	CDB	BUILD ACCESS ROAD
5	21	CDB	BUILD TO ROOF LEVEL
35	50	ASU	DELIVER FEEDERS
9	22	CDM	DELIVER MAST
15	28	PSU	DELIVER POWER UNIT
21	22		DUMMY
21	25	CDB	COMP. BUILDING TO POWER PT.
22	40	CDM	1ST STAGE MAST FABRICATION
25	28		DUMMY
25	29	CDB	COMPLETE BUILDING TO TX PT
28	30	PSU	CONNECT POWER UNIT TO H.T.
29	30		DUMMY
29	80	CDB	COMPLETE BUILDING
10	20	TSU	WORKS TEST TRANSMITTER
40	45	CDM	COMPLETE MAST
20	30	TSU	DELIVER TRANSMITTER TO SITE
30	60	TSU	INSTALL TX & CONNECT TO L.T.
60	70	TSU	MANUFACTURER TESTS TO TX.
12	55	ASU	DELIVER AERIAL
45	50	CDM	ERECT HOIST
50	55	ASU	ERECT FEEDERS
55	65	ASU	ERECT AERIALS
65	70	ASU	MANUFACTURER TESTS AERIAL
70	80	ASU	CONNECT AERIAL TO TX.
80	90	TSU	P.I.D. TEST SYSTEM
90	100	TSU	OPER. & MAINT. DEPT. TESTS
100	105	TSU	STEREO TEST
100	110	TSU	TRADE TEST
105	110		DUMMY

Case Study—Building a V.H.F. Transmitter

DUR	EARLIEST START	EARLIEST FINISH	LATEST START	LATEST FINISH	TOT FLOAT	FREE FLT
21	0T	21	0T	21	0	0
9	0T	9	35	44	35	16
63	0T	63	22	85	22	0
78	0T	78	7	85	7	0
28	0T	28	51	79	51	0
42	0T	42	38	80	38	12
21	0T	21	58	79	58	0
4	21	25	40	44	19	0
24	21	45	21	45	0	0
3	21	24	79	82	58	58
1	25	26	44	45	19	19
1	28	29	79	80	51	25
0	45	45	45	45	0	0
9	45	54	71	80	26	0
18	45	63	45	63	0	0
0	54	54	80	80	26	0
4	54	58	83	87	29	0
7	54	61	80	87	26	4
0	58	58	87	87	29	7
8	58	66	90	98	32	32
1	63	64	85	86	22	0
18	63	81	63	81	0	0
1	64	65	86	87	22	0
4	65	69	87	91	22	0
6	69	75	91	97	22	22
1	78	79	85	86	7	7
1	81	82	81	82	0	0
4	82	86	82	86	0	0
4	86	90	86	90	0	0
7	90	97	90	97	0	0
1	97	98	97	98	0	0
2	98	100	98	100	0	0
2	100	102	100	102	0	0
1	102	103	103	104	1	0
2	102	104	102	104	0	0
0	103	103	104	104	1	1

Critical Path Analysis

                         PROJECT TS   BUILDING A TRANSMITTER STATION

ACTIVITIES IN TOTAL FLOAT ORDER

PREC EVENT	SUCC EVENT	REPORT CODE	DESCRIPTION
1	5	CDB	DELIVER BUILDING MATERIALS
5	21	CDB	BUILD TO ROOF LEVEL
21	22		DUMMY
22	40	CDM	1ST STAGE MAST FABRICATION
40	45	CDM	COMPLETE MAST
45	50	CDM	ERECT HOIST
50	55	ASU	ERECT FEEDERS
55	65	ASU	ERECT AERIALS
65	70	ASU	MANUFACTURER TESTS AERIAL
70	80	ASU	CONNECT AERIAL TO TX.
80	90	TSU	P.I.D. TEST SYSTEM
90	100	TSU	OPER. & MAINT. DEPT. TESTS
100	110	TSU	TRADE TEST
100	105	TSU	STEREO TEST
105	110		DUMMY
1	12	ASU	MANUFACTURE AERIALS
12	55	ASU	DELIVER AERIAL
5	9	CDB	BUILD ACCESS ROAD
9	22	CDM	DELIVER MAST
1	10	TSU	MANUFACTURE TRANSMITTER
10	20	TSU	WORKS TEST TRANSMITTER
20	30	TSU	DELIVER TRANSMITTER TO SITE
30	60	TSU	INSTALL TX & CONNECT TO L.T.
60	70	TSU	MANUFACTURER TESTS TO TX.
21	25	CDB	COMP. BUILDING TO POWER PT.
25	28		DUMMY
28	30	PSU	CONNECT POWER UNIT TO H.T.
25	29	CDB	COMPLETE BUILDING TO TX PT
29	30		DUMMY
29	80	CDB	COMPLETE BUILDING
1	9	CDM	MANUFACTURE MAST
1	28	PSU	E. BOARD SUPPLY H.T.
1	15	PSU	MANUFACTURE POWER UNIT
15	28	PSU	DELIVER POWER UNIT
1	35	ASU	MANUFACTURE FEEDERS
35	50	ASU	DELIVER FEEDERS

Case Study—Building a V.H.F. Transmitter

DUR	EARLIEST START	EARLIEST FINISH	LATEST START	LATEST FINISH	TOT FLOAT	FREE FLT
21	0T	21	0T	21	0	0
24	21	45	21	45	0	0
0	45	45	45	45	0	0
18	45	63	45	63	0	0
18	63	81	63	81	0	0
1	81	82	81	82	0	0
4	82	86	82	86	0	0
4	86	90	86	90	0	0
7	90	97	90	97	0	0
1	97	98	97	98	0	0
2	98	100	98	100	0	0
2	100	102	100	102	0	0
2	102	104	102	104	0	0
1	102	103	103	104	1	0
0	103	103	104	104	1	1
78	0T	78	7	85	7	0
1	78	79	85	86	7	7
4	21	25	40	44	19	0
1	25	26	44	45	19	19
63	0T	63	22	85	22	0
1	63	64	85	86	22	0
1	64	65	86	87	22	0
4	65	69	87	91	22	0
6	69	75	91	97	22	22
9	45	54	71	80	26	0
0	54	54	80	80	26	0
7	54	61	80	87	26	4
4	54	58	83	87	29	0
0	58	58	87	87	29	7
8	58	66	90	98	32	32
9	0T	9	35	44	35	16
42	0T	42	38	80	38	12
28	0T	28	51	79	51	0
1	28	29	79	80	51	25
21	0T	21	58	79	58	0
3	21	24	79	82	58	58

I.C.T. 1900 SERIES PERT   24/06/68   OUTPUT SHEET NUMBER 21

   PROJECT TS BUILDING A TRANSMITTER STATION   RUN   TIME NOW 0 PAGE 1

CRITICAL PATH

PREC EVENT	SUCC EVENT	REPORT CODE	DESCRIPTION	DUR	EARLIEST START	EARLIEST FINISH	LATEST START	LATEST FINISH	TOT FLOAT	FREE FLT
1	5	CDB	DELIVER BUILDING MATERIALS	21	0	21	0	21	0	0
5	21	CDB	BUILD TO ROOF LEVEL	24	21	45	21	45	0	0
21	22		DUMMY	0	45	45	45	45	0	0
22	40	CDM	1ST STAGE MAST FABRICATION	18	45	63	45	63	0	0
40	45	CDM	COMPLETE MAST	18	63	81	63	81	0	0
45	50	CDM	ERECT HOIST	1	81	82	81	82	0	0
50	55	ASU	ERECT FEEDERS	4	82	86	82	86	0	0
55	65	ASU	ERECT AERIALS	4	86	90	86	90	0	0
65	70	ASU	MANUFACTURER TESTS AERIAL	7	90	97	90	97	0	0
70	80	ASU	CONNECT AERIAL TO TX.	1	97	98	97	98	0	0
80	90	TSU	P.I.D. TEST SYSTEM	2	98	100	98	100	0	0
90	100	TSU	OPER. & MAINT. DEPT. TESTS	2	100	102	100	102	0	0
100	110	TSU	TRADE TEST	2	102	104	102	104	0	0

PROJECT TS   BUILDING A TRANSMITTER STATION

24/06/68   RUN   TIME NOW   0   PAGE 1

BAR CHART-ACTIVITIES BY RESPONSIBILITY CODE

S/P PREC EVENT 1	SUCC EVENT I	REPORT U CODE	DESCRIPTION	DUR	4	18	32	46	60
1	35	ASU	MANUFACTURE AERIALS	78					
1	50	ASU	MANUFACTURE FEEDERS	21					
35	50	ASU	DELIVER FEEDERS	3					
12	55	ASU	DELIVER AERIAL	1					
50	55	ASU	ERECT FEEDERS	4					
55	65	ASU	ERECT AERIALS	4					
65	70	ASU	MANUFACTURER TESTS AERIAL	7					
70	80	ASU	CONNECT AERIAL TO TX.	1					

198

I.C.T. 1900 SERIES PERT   24/06/68   OUTPUT SHEET NUMBER 29

                    PROJECT TS   BUILDING A TRANSMITTER STATION   RUN   TIME NOW   0 PAGE 1

BAR CHART-ACTIVITIES BY RESPONSIBILITY CODE

        74   88   102   116   130   144   158   172
   .*....I....*....*....I....*....I....*....I....*....I....*....I....*....I....*....I....*.
    -AAAAAAAAAAAAA.........
    *   I   *   I   *   I   *   I   *   I   *   I   *   I   *   I   *
    *   I   *   I   *   I   *   I   *   I   *   I   *   I   *   I   *
   -..................
    *   I   *   I   *   I   *   I   *   I   *   I   *   I   *   I   *
    *   I   *   I   *   I   *   I   *   I   *   I   *   I   *   I   *
   -..................
    *   I   *   I   *   I   *   I   *   I   *   I   *   I   *   I   *
         A.........
    *   I   *   I   *   I   *   I   *   I   *   I   *   I   *   I   *
         CCCC
    *   I   *   I   *   I   *   I   *   I   *   I   *   I   *   I   *
         CCCC
    *   I   *   I   *   I   *   I   *   I   *   I   *   I   *   I   *
              CCCCCCC
    *   I   *   I   *   I   *   I   *   I   *   I   *   I   *   I   *
    *   I   *   I   *   I   *   I   *   I   *   I   *   I   *   I   *
                   C
    *   I   *   I   *   I   *   I   *   I   *   I   *   I   *   I   *
    *   I   *   I   *   I   *   I   *   I   *   I   *   I   *   I   *

Building a V.H.F. transmitter station
Sequenced Gantt Chart
Weeks (5 day weeks)

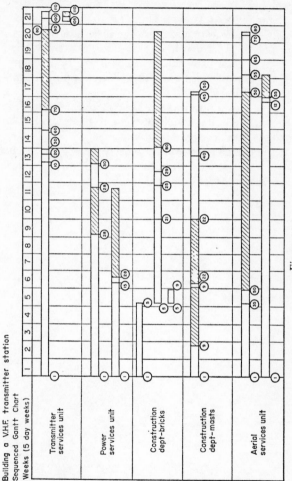

Figure 14-3

there will be six days float left in this chain. The six days will appear as free float on activity 'Manufacturer Aligns and tests Tx with Dummy Aerial'.

(b) *Deliver Mast* (9–22) has lost all its float by week 9 and hence a delay will affect the start of activity 'First Stage in Mast Fabrication', which is a critical activity. The effect of the delay will be to delay the project completion date by 1 day.

(c) There is no hurry on *Deliver Feeder* (35–50). If it does arrive in the middle of week 10 there will still be 35 days free float on this activity.

The overall effect will be to delay the project by one day, unless reductions in time are made on the critical activities not yet completed.

7. See 14.6.
8. See 14.7.

Building a V.H.F. transmitter station

Resource aggregation – earliest starts

Weeks (5 day week)

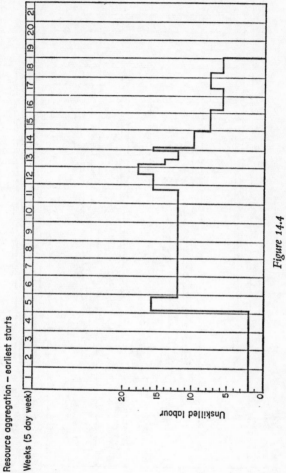

Figure 14.4

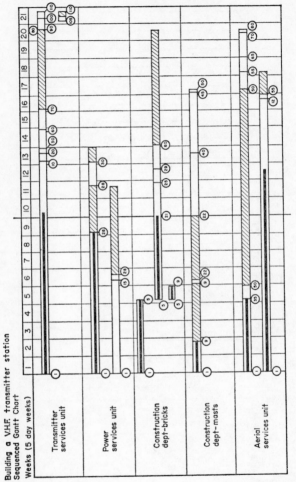

Figure 14-5

Building a V.H.F. transmitter station
activity-on-node

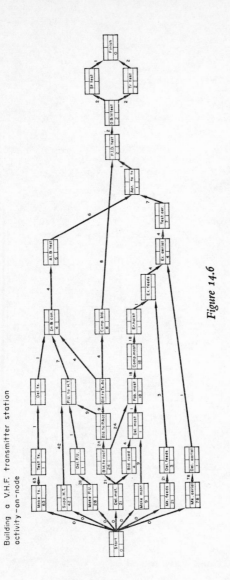

Figure 14·6

Building a V.H.F. transmitter station
activity-on-node

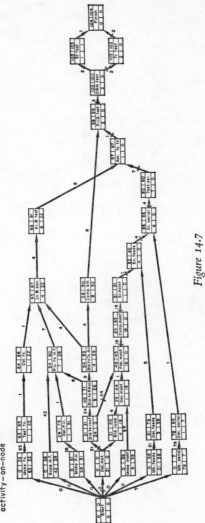

Figure 14.7